Answers to Revision Questions for Higher Chemistry

D A Buchanan
(Moray House School of Education, University of Edinburgh)

J R Melrose
(formerly Lenzie Academy)

A D Ross
(formerly Duncanrig Secondary School)

Published by
Chemcord
Inch Keith
East Kilbride
Glasgow

ISBN 9781870570978

Printed by Bell and Bain Ltd, Glasgow

Covalent and ionic radius

1. (a) Covalent radius is a measure of the size of the atom.
   (b)

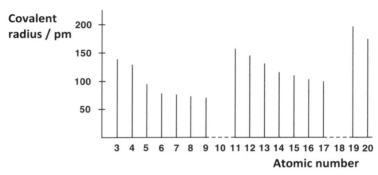

   (c) Covalent radius is a periodic property as with increasing atomic number there is a definite pattern that is repeated across the period.

2. (a) On crossing a period in the Periodic Table, from left to right, the covalent radius decreases.
   (b) On descending a group in the Periodic Table the covalent radius increases.

3. (a) Hydrogen has the smallest covalent radius of all the elements. However, more generally, elements made up of atoms with the smallest covalent radii are found in the top right part of the Periodic Table around fluorine.
   (b) Elements made up of atoms with the largest covalent radii are found in the bottom left part of the Periodic Table around caesium.

4. (a) Lithium and fluorine are in the same period. Moving across the period from lithium to fluorine electrons are being added to the same shell and protons are being added to the nucleus. The electrons in the outer shell are therefore attracted more strongly to the nucleus because of its increasing positive charge. This means that a lithium atom will be larger than a fluorine atom.
   (b) Fluorine and iodine are in the same group. Going down the group from fluorine to iodine the number of occupied electron shells is increasing. As the electron shells are progressively further from the nucleus, the atoms increase in size. This means that a fluorine atom will be smaller than an iodine atom.

5. (a) A fluoride ion (F^-) (electron arrangement 2, 8) has one less occupied shell than a chloride ion (Cl^-) (electron arrangement 2, 8, 8) and therefore will be smaller.

   (b) A lithium ion (Li^+) (electron arrangement 2) has one less shell than a fluoride ion (F^-) (electron arrangement 2, 8) and therefore will be smaller.

   (c) A potassium ion (K^+) (electron arrangement 2, 8, 8) has the same number of occupied shells, and electrons, as a calcium ion (Ca^{2+}) (electron arrangement 2, 8, 8). However, the potassium ion has fewer protons (19 compared to the 20 in calcium). The greater positive charge of the calcium nucleus pulls the electrons closer to the nucleus, and therefore the potassium ion is larger.

   (d) A chloride ion (Cl^-) (electron arrangement 2, 8, 8) has the same number of occupied shells, and electrons, as a potassium ion (K^+) (electron arrangement 2, 8, 8). However, the chloride ion has fewer protons (17 compared to the 19 in potassium). The greater positive charge of the potassium nucleus pulls the electrons closer to the nucleus, and therefore the chloride ion is larger.

6. (a) Atomic number 13 – Al^{3+} – about 0.045
   Atomic number 15 – P^{3-} – about 0.22 (but if P^{5+} – about 0.02)

   (b) i) H^+ has no electrons and is only a proton, and does not exist as an ion in a crystal lattice.
   ii) Although H^- and Li^+ both have two electrons, the greater number of protons in lithium pulls these electrons closer to the nucleus, and therefore H^- is larger than Li^+.

   (c) B^{3+} (electron arrangement 2) has only one occupied electron shell, but N^{3-} (electron arrangement 2, 8) has two occupied electron shells. Therefore, N^{3-} is much larger than B^{3+}.
   In addition, going down the group there is increased shielding (or screening) of the outer electrons from the nucleus by the inner electrons. Hence the outer electrons do feel the full 'pull' of the nucleus.

7. (a) The ions of sodium, magnesium and aluminium all have one fewer occupied electron shell than their corresponding atoms.

   (b) Al^{3+} (electron arrangement 2,8) has two occupied electron shells, but P^{3-} (electron arrangement 2,8,8) has three occupied electron shells. Therefore, P^{3-} is much larger than Al^{3+}.

   (c) i) All the ions from N^{3-} to Al^{3+} have an electron arrangement of 2, 8.
   ii) Although all the ions have the same electron arrangement, the increasing positive charge of the nuclei along the sequence from N^{3-} to Al^{3+} leads to a decrease in ionic radii.

Ionisation energy and electronegativity

1. (a) The first ionisation energy of an element is the energy required to remove one electron from the outer shell of each atom in one mole of gaseous atoms of the element.
   (b) i) The process is endothermic.
       ii) Energy is required to overcome the attraction between the positively charged nucleus and the negative electrons being removed.

2. (a) **First ionisation energy / kJ mol^{-1}**

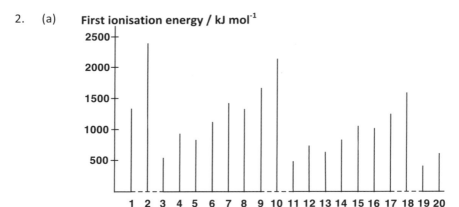

Atomic number

   (b) First ionisation energy is a periodic property as with increasing atomic number there is a definite pattern that is repeated across the period.

3. (a) First ionisation energy increases on crossing a period in the Periodic Table from left to right.
   (b) First ionisation energy decreases on descending a group in the Periodic Table.

4. (a) Lithium has a larger first ionisation energy than potassium, as the electron being removed from each atom of potassium is both further from the attraction of the positive nucleus and is shielded (or screened) from the full nuclear charge by the inner shells of electrons.
   (b) Although the electron being removed from each type of atom is in the same shell, it is more easily removed from sodium as it is attracted by a less positively charged nucleus (11 protons in a sodium atom compared with 13 protons in an aluminium atom).

5. (a) i) The second ionisation energy of lithium is much larger than the first ionisation energy since, as a Group 1 element, removal of a second electron is from a shell closer to the nucleus.

(ii) The third ionisation energy of calcium is much larger than the second ionisation energy since, as a Group 2 element, removal of a third electron is from a shell closer to the nucleus.

iii) The fourth ionisation energy of aluminium is much larger than the third ionisation energy since, as a Group 3 element, removal of a fourth electron is from a shell closer to the nucleus.

6. (a) i) $Na (g) \rightarrow Na^+ (g) + e^-$ $\Delta H = +496$ kJ mol^{-1}
    &   ii) $Mg^+ (g) \rightarrow Mg^{2+} (g) + e^-$ $\Delta H = +1451$ kJ mol^{-1}
    (b) iii) $Al^{2+} (g) \rightarrow Al^{3+} (g) + e^-$ $\Delta H = +2745$ kJ mol^{-1}

7. (a) The equation represents the sum of the 1st, 2nd and 3rd ionisation energies of aluminium.
    Therefore, energy required = 578 + 1817 + 2745 = 5140 kJ mol^{-1}

    (b) The equation represents the sum of the 2nd and 3rd ionisation energies of potassium.
    Therefore, energy required = 3052 + 4420 = 7472 kJ mol^{-1}

8. (a) Electronegativity is the measure of the attraction that the nucleus of an atom involved in a bond has for the electrons in the bond.

    (b)

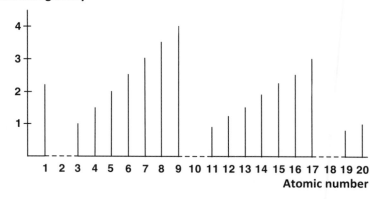

Electonegativity

    (c) Electronegativity is a periodic property as with increasing atomic number there is a definite pattern that is repeated across the period.

    (d) The Group 0 elements (the noble gases) have no quoted electronegativity values.

9. (a) On crossing a period in the Periodic Table, from left to right, the electronegativity values increase.
    (b) On descending a group in the Periodic Table, the electronegativity values decrease.

10. (a) A chlorine atom has an additional inner shell of electrons that shield (or screen) the bonding electrons from the full nuclear charge. Therefore, the bonding electrons in chlorine are less attracted to the nucleus than in fluorine, i.e. fluorine is more electronegative than chlorine.
    (b) The bonding electrons of both oxygen and fluorine are in the same shell. However, the larger positively charged nucleus of the fluorine atom increases the attraction of the nucleus for these electrons, i.e. fluorine is more electronegative than oxygen.

11. $Cl (g) + e^- \rightarrow Cl^- (g)$

Covalent and ionic bonding (revision)

1. (a) The two hydrogen atoms involved each share a pair of electrons with the sulphur atom. In this way all the atoms achieve the stable electron arrangement of a noble gas.
    (b) The shared pair of electrons between two atoms joined by a covalent bond is attracted to the positively charged nuclei of both atoms.

2. (a) An electron is transferred from the sodium atom to the chlorine atom. The resulting Na^+ and Cl^- ions both have the stable electron arrangement of a noble gas. The force of attraction between the oppositely charged ions is known as an ionic bond.
    (b) Ionic bonds are strong because large amounts of energy are required to overcome the forces of attraction between the oppositely charged ions.
    (c) Sodium chloride exists as a giant three-dimensional crystal lattice in which the ions are held together by ionic bonding. Molecules involve relatively small groups of atoms joined by covalent bonding.

3. (a) Hydrogen oxide, chlorine, fluorine, nitrogen chloride, oxygen and hydrogen sulphide are covalent molecular substances.
    (b) Sodium fluoride, potassium chloride and lithium oxide are substances with ionic lattices.

4. (a) Covalent molecular compounds have relatively small numbers of atoms in each molecule held together by covalent bonds, but with weak intermolecular forces between the molecules.
    Covalent network compounds have giant lattices of many atoms held throughout by covalent bonding.
    (b) Silicon dioxide and silicon carbide are examples of covalent network compounds.

5.

Oxide	Bonding and structure
Na_2O	ionic lattice
CO_2	covalent molecular
SiO_2	covalent network

Polar covalent bonds and the bonding continuum

1. (a) In a polar covalent bond, the bonding electrons are not equally shared but are pulled closer to one of the atoms.

   (b) i) Hydrogen and fluorine achieve stable noble gas electron arrangements by sharing a pair of electrons to form a covalent bond. However, as fluorine is more electronegative, the electrons are pulled closer to fluorine and are not shared equally. The bond is therefore a polar covalent bond.

      ii) $\overset{\delta+}{H}-\overset{\delta-}{F}$

   (c) i) H–F is a more polar bond than H–Cl.

      ii) H–F is a more polar bond because fluorine is more electronegative than chlorine.

2. (a) A molecule is said to have a permanent dipole if it has a permanent uneven distribution of charge, e.g. in a hydrogen fluoride molecule, the hydrogen atom has a permanent slight positive charge and the fluorine atom a permanent slight negative charge.

   (b) Water has polar covalent bonds. The water also has a permanent dipole with the hydrogen end slightly positive and the oxygen end slightly negative.

3. In both N_2 and H_2, the atoms form covalent bonds between two atoms of the same kind and so electrons are equally shared.

   However, in NH_3 the electrons in the covalent bonds are not equally shared as N and H have different electronegativities.

4. (a) In phosphorus hydride the electrons in the covalent bonds are shared equally because phosphorus and hydrogen have the same electronegativity (2.2).

   (b) i) Carbon disulphide, CS_2, as both elements have the same electronegativity (2.5).

      ii) Nitrogen trichloride, NCl_3, as both elements have the same electronegativity (3.5).

5.   Potassium fluoride is more ionic than lithium bromide as the elements involved have a bigger difference in electronegativity.
        [K (0.8) and F (4.0), i.e. a difference of 3.2
        Li (1.0) and Br (2.8), i.e. a difference of 1.8]

6. (a) Lithium and fluorine form the compound with the most ionic character.
    (b) These two elements have the biggest difference in electronegativity in the period. [Li (1.0) and F (4.0), i.e. a difference of 3.0]

7.   The difference in electronegativity is greater between rubidium and fluorine, than between rubidium and any other halogen.

Properties of compounds

1. (a) Ionic compounds have high melting and boiling points because a lot of energy is required to separate the oppositely charged ions in the lattice.
    (b) Ionic compounds do not conduct electricity in the solid form because the ions are not free to move. The ions are free to move in the molten state.

2. (a) Covalent molecular compounds have relatively low melting and boiling points because the bonds broken are the weak intermolecular forces. This does not require a lot of energy.
    (b) Covalent molecular compounds cannot conduct electricity in any form because they have no ions or delocalised electrons to move through the substance.

3. Covalent network compounds have very high melting points because covalent bonds are broken on melting and a lot of energy is required for this. In covalent molecular compounds only relatively weak intermolecular forces need to be broken on melting and this requires much less energy.

4. (a) covalent network
    (b) High melting points are typical of both ionic and covalent network compounds. However, if ionic the compound would conduct electricity when molten.

5. The conclusion is incorrect.
    Ionic bonds are broken when an ionic compound melts, but only weak intermolecular forces are broken when a covalent molecular substance melts or boils. The covalent bonds of the molecule are not broken and so no comparison between the relative strengths of ionic and covalent bonds can be made on this evidence.

6. Titanium chloride is likely to be covalent.
    $TiCl_4$ has a relatively low boiling point. It is unlikely to contain ionic bonds which are strong and require a lot of energy to break. The low boiling point suggests that only weak intermolecular forces have to be broken on boiling.

7. The lithium halides are ionic solids. The melting points decrease because the strength of the ionic bonds decrease. This is due to the smaller difference in electronegativity between lithium and the halogen as you go down Group 7 of the Periodic Table.

8. PCl_3 has a covalent molecular structure with only weak forces between its molecules.
NaCl is an ionic solid and has strong ionic bonds between all neighbouring ions in its lattice.

9.   (a) Boiling points: HCl −85 °C; HBr −67 °C; HI −35 °C.
All the compounds have permanent dipole-permanent dipole intermolecular forces between the molecules.
The boiling points increase as you go down the group because the strength of the intermolecular forces increases as the number of electrons present in the molecule increases, i.e. the strength of the intermolecular forces increases with increasing molecular mass.
(b) HF has a much higher than expected boiling point (+20 °C) due to it having strong hydrogen bonding between its molecules.

10. (a) Methanol and hydrazine contain hydrogen bonding in the liquid state.
(b) Hydrogen bonding is a relatively strong intermolecular force. More energy is required separate the molecules.
(c) Substances of similar molecular mass will have comparable strength of London dispersion forces between the molecules.

11. Both compounds are covalent molecular substances.
Liquid phosphine (PH_3) has a low boiling point because the forces holding molecules together are only weak London dispersion forces.
[P and H have the same electronegativity − 2.2]
Liquid ammonia (NH_3), which has a lower molecular mass, has a much higher boiling point because hydrogen bonding occurs between its much more polar molecules. [electronegativities N − 3.0; H − 2.2]

12. H_2O_2 has strong hydrogen bonding between its highly polar molecules giving it a relatively high boiling point. Although H_2S has a similar molecular mass, it is a much less polar molecule with weaker intermolecular forces and hence a much lower boiling point.

13. (a) As you go down Group 4 of the Periodic Table, both the masses of the hydrides and the number of electrons in their molecules increase. These factors increase the strength of the London dispersion forces and therefore the boiling points of the hydrides.
(b) Water has strong hydrogen bonding between the molecules. This type of intermolecular force is not present in the other Group 6 hydrides and therefore the considerably higher than expected boiling point of water.

14.   Propan-1-ol will have the higher boiling point.
        Propan-1-ol has strong hydrogen bonding between its molecules due to the highly polar −OH group. Methoxyethane has only weak London dispersion forces between its molecules.

15. (a) The boiling points of the alkanes increase with increasing molecular mass because the heavier molecules have more electrons leading to stronger London dispersion forces between the molecules.
    (b) Alcohols have hydrogen bonding between the molecules.
    (c) i) The boiling point of propan-1-ol should be compared with butane.
        ii) Propan-1-ol (C_3H_7OH) is the alcohol with molecular mass closest to the molecular mass of butane (C_4H_{10}), 60 and 58 respectively.

16. (a) In octane the only forces between the molecules are London dispersion forces. However, both maleic and fumaric acids have strong hydrogen bonding between the molecules giving much higher melting points.
    (b) Fumaric acid has a much more open structure that allows more extensive hydrogen bonding between neighbouring molecules. The less open structure of maleic acid means that only one −OH group is able to be involved in hydrogen bonding across molecules, so that hydrogen bonding is less extensive.

17.   Paraffin wax has heavier molecules than petrol. Heavier molecules have more electrons and therefore stronger London dispersion forces between the molecules giving paraffin wax a higher melting point than petrol.

18.   As the temperature of water falls from 4 °C to 0 °C, its density decreases with the formation of ice. This is due to the water molecules moving further apart to form an open and rigid structure held together by hydrogen bonding. The less dense ice will float on water.

19.   Petrol has only weak London dispersion forces between its molecules. Methanol, which contains the polar −OH group, has strong hydrogen bonding between its molecules giving it a higher boiling point and making it less volatile.

20. (a) The viscosity of liquids can be determined by measuring the time taken for a known volume of liquid to pass through a small opening, e.g. from a burette. The more viscous liquids take more time to pass through.
    (b)   Ethanol   −   ethane-1,2-diol   −   propane-1,2,3-triol
        (Lowest viscosity)   (Highest viscosity)

21. Ionic compounds, e.g. sodium chloride, are soluble in water as a result of the polar nature of water. The slight negative ends of the polar water molecules are attracted to the Na^+ ions in the lattice, while the slight positive ends of the water molecules are attracted to the Cl^- ions. The electrostatic attractions between the ions and the water molecules result in a release of energy. This amount of energy is sufficient to overcome electrostatic attractions between the oppositely charged ions in the lattice, breaking up the lattice and resulting in the formation of hydrated ions.

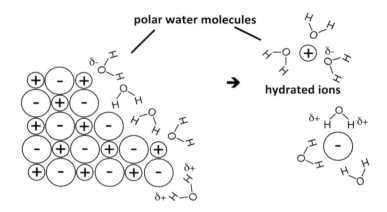

22. (a) The positive and negative ions of potassium fluoride can interact with the negative and positive ends of the surrounding polar water molecules. This process releases energy which compensates for the energy needed to break up the ionic lattice.

Hexane is non-polar and cannot interact strongly enough with the ions of potassium chloride to break up the lattice.

(b) Tetrachloromethane dissolves in hexane because new London dispersion forces between tetrachloromethane and hexane can replace the existing London dispersion forces broken in the two pure non-polar liquids when they mix.

If non-polar tetrachloromethane is mixed with polar water, there is no strong interaction between the molecules to release the energy needed to compensate for the breaking of the strong hydrogen bonding in water. Therefore, tetrachloromethane will not mix with water.

9.   (a)   **70 minutes**   [*Any answer between 68 and 72 would be acceptable.*]
     (b)   i) sample **A**   ii) sample **B**
     (c)   Sample **A** has the higher purity because it produced the greater volume of
           gas indicating a greater amount of calcium carbonate in the 0.5 g sample.
           Sample **B** has the smaller particle size because the initial rate of reaction
           is faster than with Sample **A**.

10. (a)   From the information in the results table, it can be stated that the volume
           of hydrochloric acid, the total volume of all reactants and the
           concentration of the hydrochloric acid were all kept constant through the
           series of experiments.
     (b)   i)   The purpose of the investigation was to determine the effect of
           changing the concentration of sodium thiosulphate solution on its rate of
           reaction with hydrochloric acid.
           ii) As the concentration of the sodium thiosulphate increased the rate of
           its reaction with hydrochloric acid increased.
           [The highest concentration sodium thiosulphate solution obscured the
           cross in the shortest time, i.e. at the fastest rate.]

Hydrocarbons (revision)

1. (a) 2-methylpentane   (b) 2,3-dimethylbutane
   (c) 3-methylpentane   (d) 2,2-dimethylbutane
   (e) 4-ethyl-5-methylhex-1-ene   (f) 3,3-dimethylbut-1-ene
   (g) 3,6-dimethylhept-3-ene   (h) methylcyclobutane
   (i) 2-ethylbut-1-ene   (j) 1,2-dimethylcyclohexane
   (k) 3-methylbut-1-ene   (l) 2,3-dimethylcyclopentene

2. (a)

$$CH_3-\overset{\displaystyle H}{\underset{\displaystyle CH_3}{C}}-CH_3$$

(b)

$$CH_3-CH_2-\overset{\displaystyle H}{\underset{\displaystyle \underset{\displaystyle CH_3}{CH_2}}{C}}-CH_2-CH_2-CH_3$$

(c)

$$CH_3-\overset{\displaystyle CH_3}{\underset{\displaystyle CH_3}{C}}-CH_2-\overset{\displaystyle CH_3}{\underset{\displaystyle H}{C}}-CH_3$$

(d)

$$CH_3-\overset{\displaystyle CH_3}{\underset{\displaystyle H}{C}}-\overset{\displaystyle H}{\underset{\displaystyle \underset{\displaystyle CH_3}{CH_2}}{C}}-CH_2-CH_2-CH_2-CH_3$$

(e) $CH_3-CH_2-CH_2-CH=CH_2$

(f)

$$CH_2=CH-CH_2-\overset{\displaystyle CH_3}{\underset{\displaystyle CH_3}{C}}-CH_2-CH_2-CH_2-CH_3$$

(g)

$$CH_3-C=\overset{\displaystyle CH_3}{\underset{\displaystyle CH_3}{C}}-CH_3$$

(h)

$$CH_3-\overset{\displaystyle H}{C}=\overset{\displaystyle H}{\underset{\displaystyle CH_3}{C}}-CH_2-CH_3$$

(i)

$$CH_2=\overset{\displaystyle H}{C}-\overset{\displaystyle H}{C}=\overset{\displaystyle H}{C}-CH_3$$

(j)

$$\begin{array}{c} CH_2 \\ H_2C \diagup \quad \diagdown CH-CH_2-CH_3 \\ H_2C \diagdown \quad \diagup CH_2 \\ CH_2 \end{array}$$

(k)

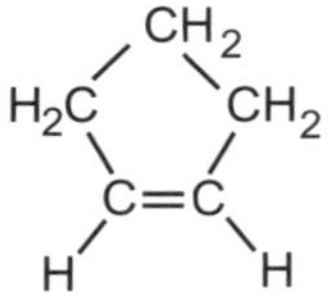

(l)

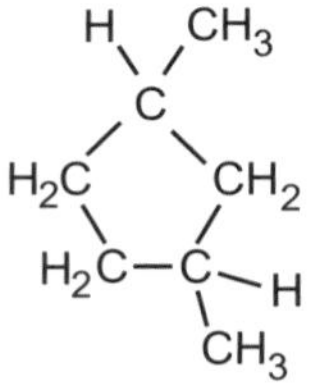

3. (a) ethane is C_2H_6 – C:H ratio = 2/6 = **0.33**
    (b) methylpropane is C_4H_{10} – C:H ratio = 4/10 = **0.4**
    (c) 3,3-dimethylhex-1-ene is C_8H_{16} – C:H ratio = 8/16 = **0.5**
    (d) methylcyclohexane is C_7H_{14} – C:H ratio = 7/14 = **0.5**
    (e) cyclopentene is C_5H_8 – C:H ratio = 5/8 = **0.625**
    (f) buta-1,3-diene is C_4H_6 – C:H ratio = 4/6 = **0.67**

4. (a) 3,3-dimethylpentane   (b) 2,3,4-trimethylpentane
    (c) 2,3-dimethylpentane   (d) dimethylpropane
    (e) but-1-ene   (f) 4,4-dimethylpent-2-ene
    (g) methylpropene   (h) 3,3-dimethylbut-1-ene

5. (a) $CH_3-CH=CH-CH_2-CH_2-CH_3$

    $CH_2=CH-CH_2-CH_2-CH_2-CH_3$

    $CH_3-CH_3-CH=CH-CH_2-CH_3$

    (b) $CH_3-CH=CH-CH=CH_2$ $CH_2=CH-CH_2-CH=CH_2$

    (c) $CH_3-CH_2-CH_2-CH_2-CH_3$

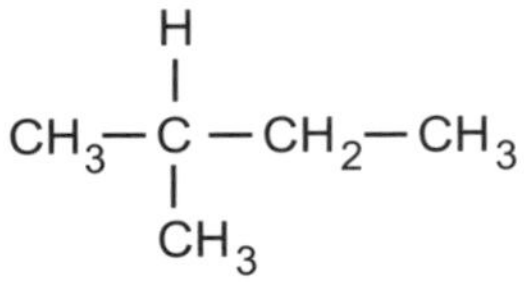

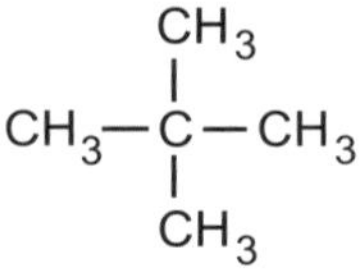

    (d) $CH_3-CH_2-CH=CH_2$ $CH_3-CH=CH-CH_3$

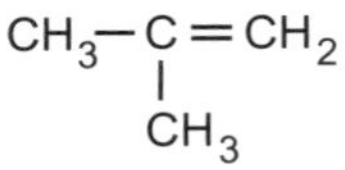

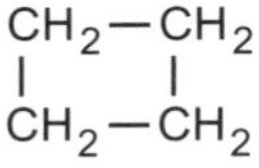

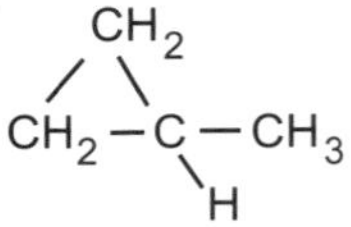

Reactions of alkenes (revision)

1. (a) Hydrocarbon **Y** is unsaturated with one carbon-carbon double bond. As a straight-chain hydrocarbon with four carbon atoms per molecule it is either but-1-ene or but-2-ene.

   (b) As unbranched hydrocarbon **Z** does not decolourise bromine solution immediately it is either an alkane or cycloalkane. With six carbon atoms per molecule it is either hexane or cyclohexane.

2. **Example:**

   $CH_2{=}CH{-}CH_2{-}CH_2{-}CH_2{-}CH_3$

   B Example:

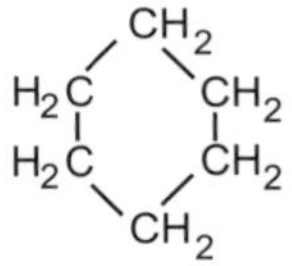

   C Example:

   $CH_2{=}CH{-}CH{=}CH{-}CH_2{-}CH_3$

   D Example:

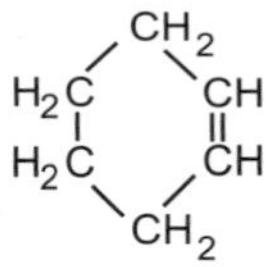

3. (a) i)

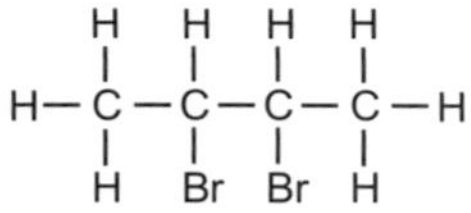

   ii)

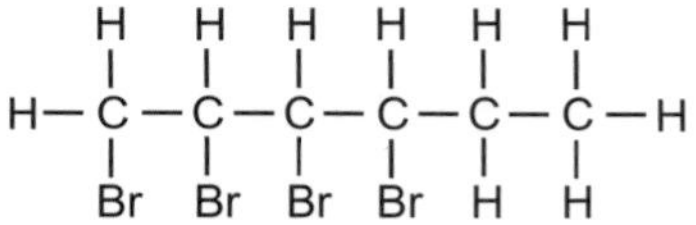

   (b) An addition reaction takes place. [The bromine atoms from the molecule are added across the double bond.]

4. (a)

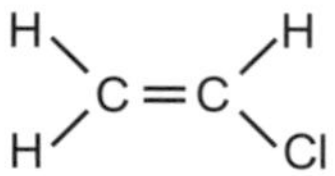

   (b) hydrogen chloride

5. (a) an addition reaction

    (b) i)

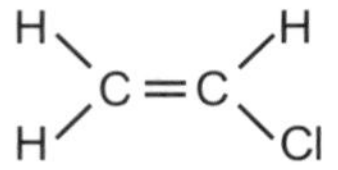

    H   H
     \   /
      C = C
     /   \
    H   Cl

    ii)

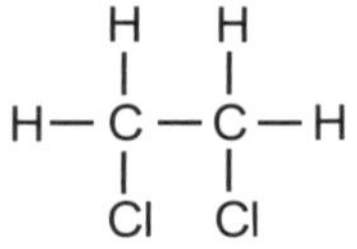

    H   H
    | |
    H—C—C—H
    | |
    Cl Cl

    iii)

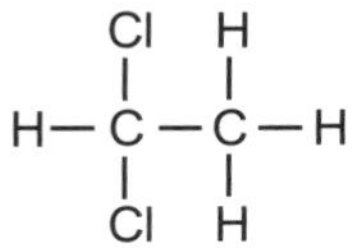

    Cl H
    | |
    H—C—C—H
    | |
    Cl H

6. (a) P

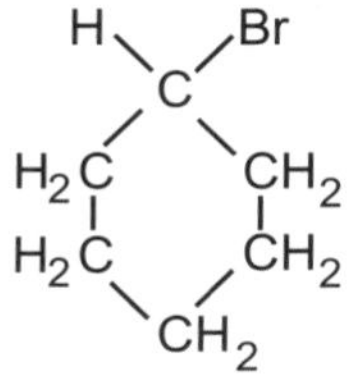

    H   Br
     \   /
       C
      /   \
    H₂C   CH₂
    | |
    H₂C   CH₂
      \   /
       CH₂

    Q

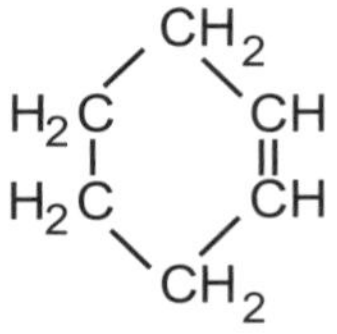

          CH₂
         /   \
    H₂C   CH
    | ‖
    H₂C   CH
         \   /
          CH₂

    R

          CH₂
         /   \
    H₂C   CH₂
    | |
    H₂C   CH₂
         \   /
          CH₂

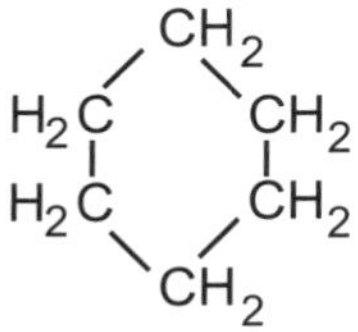

    (b) hydrogen bromide

Alcohols

1. (a) ethanol   (b) butan-2-ol
   (c) 2-methylbutan-2-ol   (d) 4-methylpentan-2-ol
   (e) 3-methylpentan-3-ol   (f) 3-methylbutan-2-ol

2. (a) $CH_3-CH_2-CH_2-CH_2-OH$ (b)

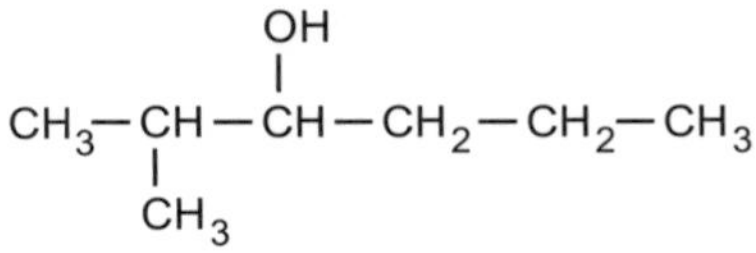

$$CH_3-CH-CH-CH_2-CH_2-CH_3$$
with OH on the second carbon and CH_3 on the third carbon

(c)

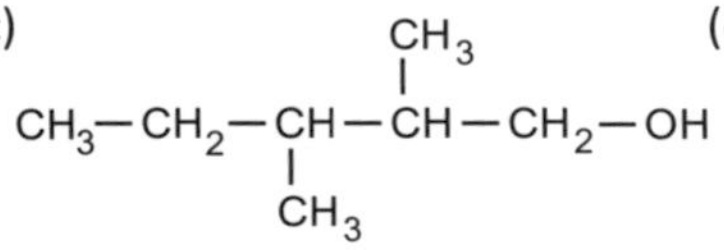

$$CH_3-CH_2-CH-CH-CH_2-OH$$
with CH_3 above the third carbon and CH_3 below the fourth carbon

(d)

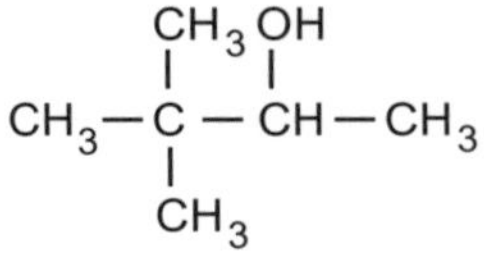

$$CH_3-C-CH-CH_3$$
with CH_3 and OH above, and CH_3 below the central carbon

3. (a)

$$H-C-C-H$$
with OH OH above and H H below the two carbons

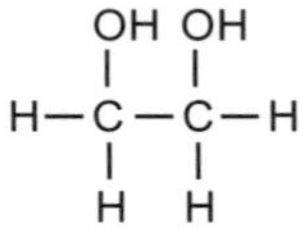

(b) A dihydric alcohol has two hydroxyl (–OH) groups in each molecule.

4. (a) $CH_3-CH_2-CH_2-CH_2-OH$

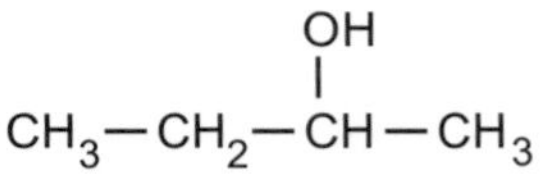

$$CH_3-CH_2-CH-CH_3$$
with OH above the third carbon

(b)

$$CH_3-CH-CH_2-OH$$
with CH_3 above the second carbon

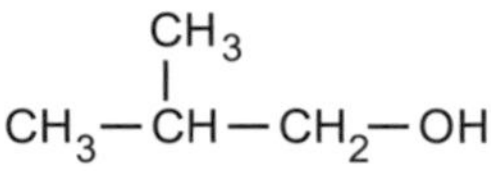

5. (a) ethanol
   (b) hydration
   [Do not confuse with hydrolysis in which the addition of atoms of water result in a splitting of the reactant molecule.]

6. (a) i) $CH_3-CH_2-CH=CH_2$ $CH_3-CH=CH-CH_3$

   ii) dehydration
   (b) [Do not confuse with condensation in which the atoms that are eliminated to make water come from the one molecule and there is no joining up of molecules.]
   i) pentan-1-ol and pentan-3-ol
   ii) pentan-2-ol

Carboxylic acids

1. (a) methanoic acid   (b) 3-methylbutanoic acid
   (c) 3-methylpentanoic acid   (d) propanoic acid
   (e) 3,3-dimethylpentanoic acid   (f) 2,3-dimethylbutanoic acid

2. (a)

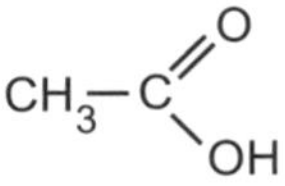

(b)

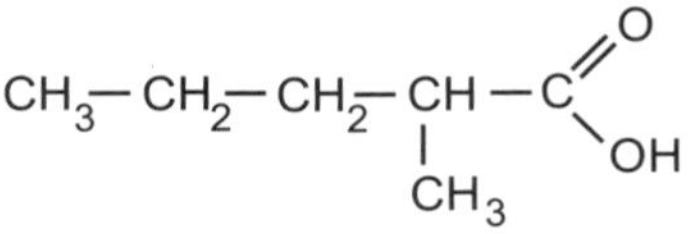

(c)

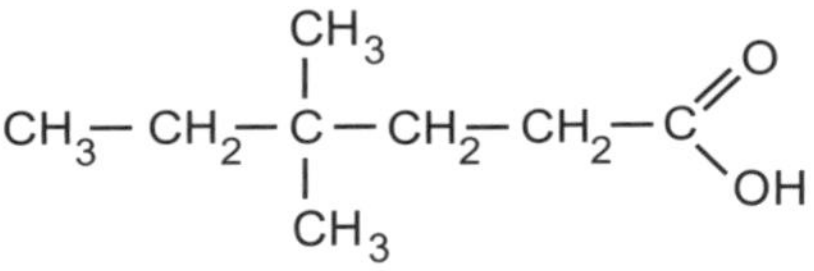

3. (a)

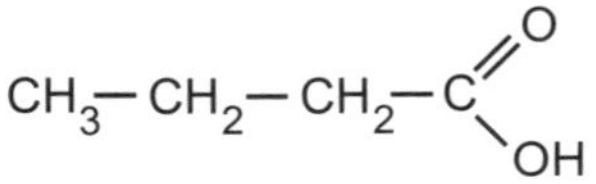

(b)

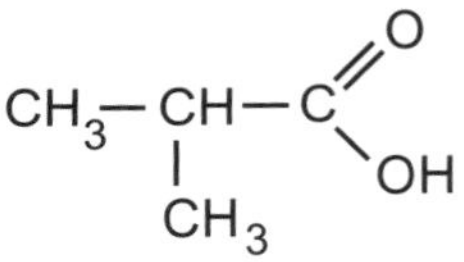

4. (a) magnesium + ethanoic acid → magnesium ethanoate + hydrogen
   $Mg + 2 CH_3COOH \rightarrow Mg(CH_3COO)_2 + H_2$
   [$Mg(CH_3COO)_2$ can be written showing ions as $Mg^{2+}(CH_3COO^-)_2$.]
   (b) sodium hydroxide + methanoic acid → sodium methanoate + water
   $NaOH + HCOOH \rightarrow NaHCOO + H_2O$
   [$NaHCOO$ can be written showing ions as Na^+HCOO^-.]
   (c) copper(II) oxide + propanoic acid → copper(II) propanoate + water
   $CuO + 2 CH_3CH_2COOH \rightarrow Cu(CH_3CH_2COO)_2 + H_2O$
   [$Cu(CH_3CH_2COO)_2$ can be written showing ions as $Cu^{2+}(CH_3CH_2COO^-)_2$
   and propanoic acid as C_2H_5COOH.]
   (d) potassium + butanoic → potassium + carbon dioxide + water
      carbonate   acid   butanoate
   $K_2CO_3 + 2 CH_3CH_2CH_2COOH \rightarrow 2 KCH_3CH_2CH_2COO + CO_2 + H_2O$
   [$KCH_3CH_2CH_2COO$ can be written showing ions as $K^+CH_3CH_2CH_2COO^-$ and
   butanoic acid as C_3H_7COOH.]

Esters (i)

1. (a) methyl ethanoate (b) methyl methanoate
    (c) propyl ethanoate (d) ethyl methanoate

2. (a)

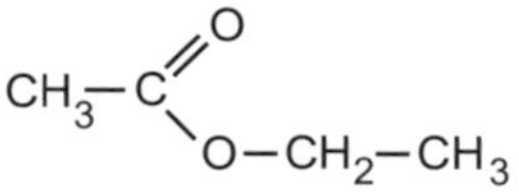

CH_3-C with =O and $O-CH_2-CH_3$

(b) $CH_3-CH_2-CH_3-C$ with =O and $O-CH_2-CH_2-CH_3$

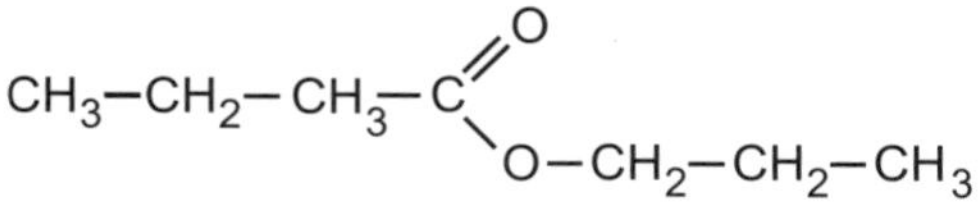

3. (a) ethyl methanoate (b) methyl propanoate
    (c) ethyl ethanoate (d) propyl methanoate

4. (a) ethanol and propanoic acid (b) methanol and ethanoic acid
    (c) ethanol and methanoic acid (d) methanol and butanoic acid

5. (a) methyl methanoate (b) methanol and methanoic acid

6.   butan-2-ol and ethanoic acid

7. (a)

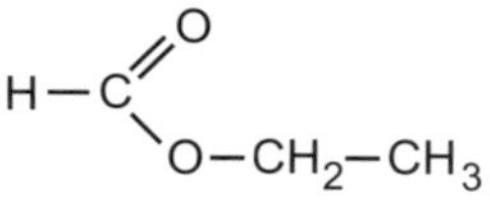

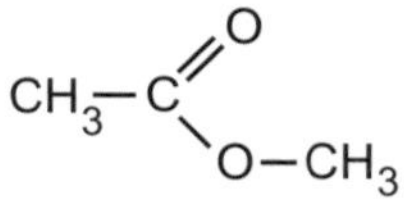

$H-C$ with =O and $O-CH_2-CH_3$

CH_3-C with =O and $O-CH_3$

    (b) ethyl methanoate   methyl ethanoate

Esters (ii)

1. (a) a condensation reaction
     [It is also referred to as an esterification.]
   (b) **X** contains ethanol and ethanoic acid.
       Y is ethyl ethanoate.

2. (a)

   (b) i) Hydrolysis involves the breakdown of a larger molecule to give smaller
          molecules due to the addition of the atoms present in water.
          [Do not confuse with a hydration reaction which also involves the
          addition of the atoms present in water, but does not involve the
          breakdown of a larger molecule.]
       ii)

       iii) Hydrolysis of aspirin by heat and moisture forms ethanoic acid.
            Ethanoic acid smells of vinegar.

3.

4. (a) 3. Add a few drops of concentrated sulphuric acid to the mixture in the test tube.
        4. Place the test tube in a hot water bath.
    (b) The paper soaked in water acts as a condenser, changing any evaporating substance back to liquid and returning to the reacting mixture.
    (c) When the contents of the test tube are poured into the beaker containing sodium hydrogencarbonate solution, an oily layer of the ester will form on the surface.
    (d) Sodium hydrogencarbonate solution is alkaline and will neutralise any unreacted acid.

5. (a) Esters are commonly found in perfumes because they have attractive fragrances and evaporate relatively easily.
    (b) i) Esters are made up of relatively non-polar molecules. As a result, they are insoluble in water, but are good solvents for many covalent compounds that are also insoluble in water.
        ii) Esters are used as solvents for many paints, varnishes and glues and as nail-polish remover.

Fats and oils

1. (a) The main purpose of fats and oils in the diet is to provide energy.
        They are also essential for the transport and storage in the body of fat
        soluble / water insoluble vitamins.
    (b) The saturated fat molecules are more closely packed. As a result the
        intermolecular forces (London dispersion forces) are relatively strong
        and fats have relatively high melting points.
        The shape of the unsaturated oil molecules does not allow such close
        packing. Consequently the London dispersion forces are weaker and the
        melting points of oils are lower than fats.

2. (a)

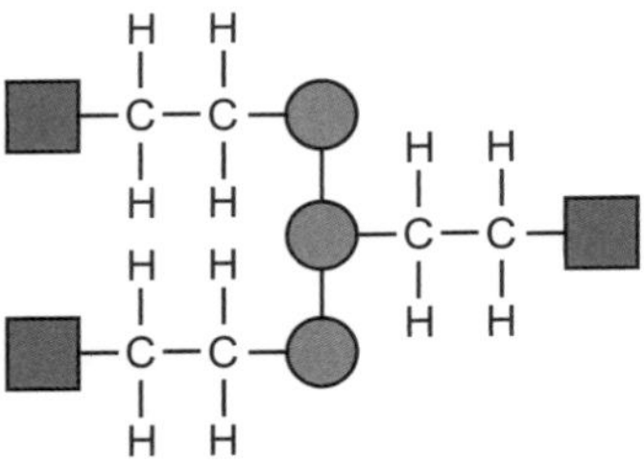

    (b) The melting point is increased by hardening.
    (c) The kind of chemical reaction that takes place during hardening is a
        (catalytic) **hydrogenation**.

3. (a) CH_2-OH
        $CH-OH$
        CH_2-OH

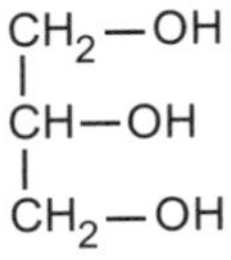

    (b) The ratio of glycerol molecules to fatty acid molecules is **1:3**.

4. (a) Triglycerides are **esters**.
    (b)

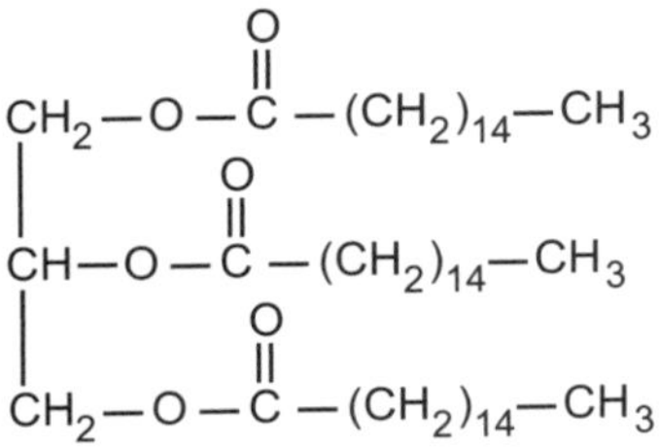

    (c) It is likely to be a **fat** because the carbon chains are saturated and will
        close pack.

5. (a) The breakdown of tristearin (an ester) is a **hydrolysis** reaction.
    (b) i) saturated
         ii) The other product of the hydrolysis reaction is **glycerol (propane-1,2,3-triol)**.

6. (a) The type of reaction that takes place when fats and oils are broken down is **hydrolysis**.
    (b) The second step of the soap making reaction is a **neutralisation** reaction. The fatty acid molecules produced by the hydrolysis of the fat or oil react with an alkali to produce a sodium salt of the fatty acid, i.e. soap.

7. (a) The compounds that are the main constituents of soap are sodium salts of long chain fatty acids.

The compounds are ionic. The negative ions have a long, non-polar, covalent carbon tail and a carboxylate head. The positive ion (Na^+) comes from the alkali used in the hydrolysis of a fat or oil.
    (b) The non-polar tails of the soap molecules are hydrophobic and dissolve in the non-polar oil. The hydrophilic heads of the soap dissolve in the water. On shaking the oil is broken up into tiny 'balls' and flushed away by the movement of the water.

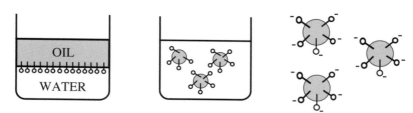

8. (a) Hydrophobic substances are insoluble in water, but readily soluble in non-polar solvents.
    (b) Hydrophilic substances are soluble in water.

9. (a) Hard water is water containing a high concentration of calcium ions (Ca^{2+}) and/or magnesium ions (Mg^{2+}).
    (b) Hard water forms a scum with soap rather than a lather.
    (c) Detergents have soap-like structures but do not react with the calcium and/or magnesium ions in hard water to form insoluble salts.

10. (a) Both soap and detergent molecules have hydrophobic tails and hydrophilic heads.
The head of the negative ion in a detergent is different from that in a soap.

soap ⌇⌇⌇⌇⌇⌇⌇⌇ $COO^- Na^+$

detergent ⌇⌇⌇⌇⌇ ◯ $-SO_3^- Na^+$

(b) As a result, soap molecules react with calcium and/or magnesium ions in hard water to form a scum (insoluble salts) and not a lather.
Detergent molecules do not react with calcium and/or magnesium ions in hard water.

11. (a) An emulsion is a mixture of two or more liquids that are normally immiscible (unmixable).
(b) Egg yolk is an emulsifier. Part of the emulsifier molecule is polar and dissolves in the vinegar. Other parts of the molecule are non-polar and dissolve in the non-polar oil. The egg yolk therefore prevents the vinegar and oil in the mayonnaise from separating.

12. The compound has two polar hydroxyl (−OH) groups. This makes the compound soluble in water. The long carbon chains in the fatty acid part of the molecule are non-polar making the compound soluble in non-polar compounds like oils. These properties allow the compound to act as an emulsifier keeping the components of the ice cream from separating and giving it a smooth texture.

Proteins

1. (a) Proteins are the major structural material of animal tissue and are essential for growth and repair.
    They are also involved in cellular processes that are essential for the maintenance and regulation of life.
    (b) The hydrolysis of proteins produces **amino acids**.
    (c) The four elements found in all proteins are **carbon, nitrogen, hydrogen** and **oxygen**.

2. (a)

    $$-\overset{\displaystyle \overset{H}{|}}{N}-CH_2-\overset{\displaystyle \overset{O}{\|}}{C}-\overset{\displaystyle \overset{H}{|}}{N}-CH_2-\overset{\displaystyle \overset{O}{\|}}{C}-\overset{\displaystyle \overset{H}{|}}{N}-CH_2-\overset{\displaystyle \overset{O}{\|}}{C}-$$

    (b) A **condensation polymerisation** reaction takes place in the joining of amino acids to form a protein.
    (c) Amino acids that the body cannot make and must be supplied in the form of dietary protein are called **essential** amino acids.

3. (a)

    $$-\overset{\displaystyle \overset{O}{\|}}{C}-\overset{\displaystyle \overset{H}{|}}{N}-$$

    (b) i) two

    ii)

    $$H-\overset{\displaystyle \overset{H}{|}}{N}-CH_2-\overset{\displaystyle \overset{O}{\|}}{C}-OH \qquad H-\overset{\displaystyle \overset{H}{|}}{N}-\underset{\displaystyle \underset{CH_3}{|}}{\overset{\displaystyle \overset{H}{|}}{C}}-\overset{\displaystyle \overset{O}{\|}}{C}-OH$$

    iii) The breakdown of a protein involves a **hydrolysis** reaction.

4. (a) Enzymes are **proteins.**
   (b)

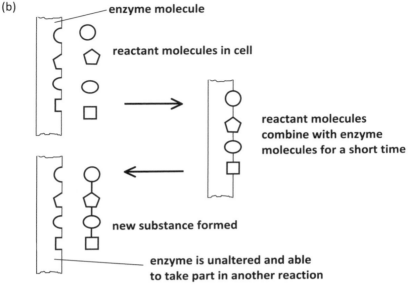

5. (a)

$$CH_3-O-\overset{\overset{\displaystyle O}{\|}}{C}-\underset{\underset{\displaystyle CH_2}{|}}{CH}-NH_2$$

$$HO-\overset{\overset{\displaystyle O}{\|}}{C}-\underset{\underset{\displaystyle NH_2}{|}}{CH}-CH_2-\overset{\overset{\displaystyle O}{\|}}{C}-OH$$

   (b) Cooking would hydrolyse aspartame and its sweetness would be lost. In cold drinks, hydrolysis is very slow and aspartame remains unchanged.

6. (a) The maltose molecule is the correct shape to exactly complement the shape of the enzyme molecule. This allows them to fit together like a "lock-and-key" bringing about the reaction.
   The sucrose molecule is not the correct shape for the enzyme and so no reaction occurs.
   (b) The shape of the maltase molecule is changed by the acidic conditions and it can no longer catalyse the reaction. This process is called **denaturing.**
   (c) Changes in pH can also affect the efficiency of an enzyme.

Plastics and fibres

1. (a) **A** is a **diamino** compound (diamine).
   B is a **dicarboxylic acid**.
   (b) condensation polymerisation
   (c)

$$-\overset{\overset{O}{\|}}{C}-\underset{}{\bigcirc}-\overset{O}{\underset{\|}{C}}-\overset{H}{\underset{|}{N}}-CH_2-CH_2-\overset{H}{\underset{|}{N}}-\overset{O}{\underset{\|}{C}}-\bigcirc-\overset{O}{\underset{\|}{C}}-\overset{H}{\underset{|}{N}}-CH_2-CH_2-\overset{H}{\underset{|}{N}}-$$

2. (a) **Water** is often the small molecule product of a condensation reaction.
   (b)

$$-O-\overset{\overset{O}{\|}}{C}-\bigcirc-\overset{\overset{O}{\|}}{C}-O-CH_2-CH_2-O-\overset{\overset{O}{\|}}{C}-\bigcirc-\overset{\overset{O}{\|}}{C}-O-CH_2-CH_2-O-$$

   (c) condensation polymerisation

3. (a)

$$-\overset{\overset{O}{\|}}{C}-(CH_2)_4-\overset{\overset{O}{\|}}{C}-O-CH_2-CH_2-O$$

   (b)

$$HO-\overset{\overset{O}{\|}}{C}-(CH_2)_4-\overset{\overset{O}{\|}}{C}-OH \qquad HO-CH_2-CH_2-OH$$

4. (a) i) *Only **one** product formed with a functional group at each end.*

$$H-\overset{H}{\underset{|}{N}}-CH_2-CH_2-CH_2-CH_2-CH_2-\overset{\overset{O}{\|}}{C}-OH$$

   ii)

$$-\overset{H}{\underset{|}{N}}-CH_2-CH_2-CH_2-CH_2-CH_2-\overset{\overset{O}{\|}}{C}-\overset{H}{\underset{|}{N}}-CH_2-CH_2-CH_2-CH_2-CH_2-\overset{\overset{O}{\|}}{C}-\overset{H}{\underset{|}{N}}-CH_2-CH_2-CH_2-CH_2-CH_2-\overset{\overset{O}{\|}}{C}-$$

   (b) i)

$$-\overset{H}{\underset{|}{N}}-(CH_2)_6-\overset{H}{\underset{|}{N}}-\overset{\overset{O}{\|}}{C}-(CH_2)_6-\overset{\overset{O}{\|}}{C}-$$

   ii)

$$H-\overset{H}{\underset{|}{N}}-(CH_2)_6-\overset{H}{\underset{|}{N}}-H \qquad HO-\overset{\overset{O}{\|}}{C}-(CH_2)_6-\overset{\overset{O}{\|}}{C}-OH$$

   iii) a condensation polymer

Carbonyl compounds

1. (a) propanal
    (c) 3-methylbutanal
    (e) ethanal
    (g) 2-methylbutanal

    (b) pentan-2-one
    (d) 4,4-dimethylpentan-2-one
    (f) butan-2-one
    (h) 4,4-dimethylpentan-2-one

2. (a)
$$\underset{H-C-H}{\overset{\displaystyle O}{\overset{\|}{}}}$$

    (b)
$$\underset{CH_3-C-CH_3}{\overset{\displaystyle O}{\overset{\|}{}}}$$

    (c)
$$CH_3-CH_2-CH_2-\underset{\underset{CH_3}{\overset{|}{CH_2}}}{\overset{|}{CH}}-CH_2-\overset{\overset{H}{|}}{C}=O$$

    (d)
$$CH_3-CH_2-CH_2-\underset{\underset{CH_3}{|}}{\overset{\overset{CH_3}{|}}{C}}-\overset{\overset{O}{\|}}{C}-CH_3$$

3. (a)
$$CH_3-CH_2-CH_2-CH_2-\overset{\overset{H}{|}}{C}=O$$

$$CH_3-CH_2-\overset{\overset{O}{\|}}{C}-CH_2-CH_3$$

    (b)   pentanal

    pentan-3-one

4. (a)
$$CH_3-CH_2-\overset{\overset{H}{|}}{C}=O$$

    (b) Propanal is an **aldehyde**.
    [The carbonyl group (–C=O) is on the end carbon of the chain.]
    (c) i) Propanal does **not** have an isomer that belongs to the same homologous series.
    ii) An aldehyde must have the carbonyl group on an end carbon, and no other structure can exist for the aldehyde as a branch is not possible when the molecule has only three carbons in total.
    (d) i)
$$CH_3-\overset{\overset{O}{\|}}{C}-CH_3$$
    ii) This isomer (propanone) is a **ketone**.
    [The carbonyl group (–C=O) is **not** on the end carbon of the chain.]

5. (a) the aldehydes
    (b) i) methanal and ethanal
    ii) Any straight chain alkene with an even number of carbons and the C=C double bond in the middle of the chain would react in this way to give **one** product only, e.g. **but-2-ene** or **hex-3-ene**.

Primary, secondary and tertiary alcohols

1. (a) primary
      [Carbon with hydroxyl group
      (-OH) is **directly attached** to
      only **1** other carbon.]

   (c) secondary
      [Carbon with hydroxyl group
      (-OH) is **directly attached** to
      2 other carbons.]

   (e) primary

   (b) tertiary
      [Carbon with hydroxyl group
      (-OH) is **directly attached** to
      3 other carbons.]

   (d) primary

   (f) secondary

2. (a) secondary
   (c) primary
   (e) tertiary
      [Note: ethyl group can only
      be on the 3rd carbon of the
      chain or the molecule would
      be 4-methylhexan-3-ol or
      heptan-3-ol.]

   (b) primary
   (d) secondary
   (f) tertiary

3.   primary   secondary

   Examples:

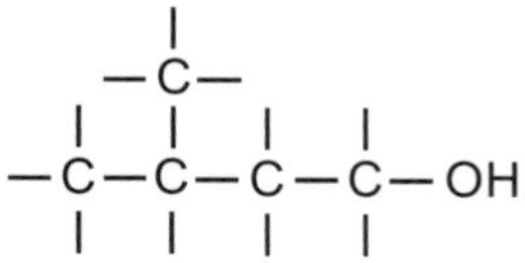

   [Note: Other structures with
   the –OH group on a different
   end carbon are also possible.]

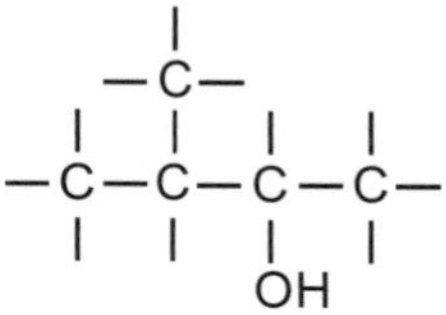

   [Note: No other structures are
   possible in this case.]

   tertiary

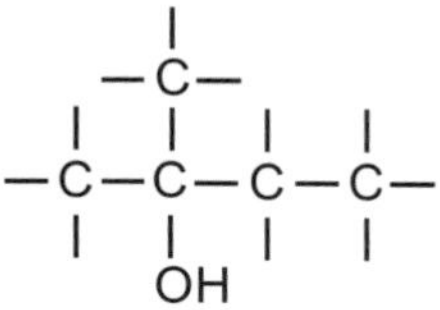

   [Note: No other structures
   are possible in this case.]

Oxidation of carbon compounds

1. (a) A **primary** alcohol can be oxidised to produce an aldehyde.
    (b) A **secondary** alcohol can be oxidised to produce a ketone.
    (c) A **tertiary** alcohol cannot be oxidised to produce a carbonyl compound.

2. (a) **Acidified dichromate solution** or **hot copper(II) oxide** are oxidising agents that can be used to produce a carbonyl compound from an alcohol.
    (b) With the **acidified dichromate solution,** the **orange** colour changes to a **blue-green** colour.
         The **black copper(II) oxide** is reduced to **red-brown** copper.

3. (a) methanol

    (b) butan-1-ol
         [Note: butanol is **not** an acceptable answer as butan-2-ol would give butanone.]

    (c) pentan-2-ol

    (d) pentan-3-ol

4. (a)
    $$CH_3-CH_2-CH_2-CH_2-CH_2-\overset{\overset{\displaystyle H}{|}}{C}=O$$

    (b)
    $$CH_3-CH_2-CH_2-CH_2-\overset{\overset{\displaystyle O}{||}}{C}-CH_3$$

5. (a) **Fehling's solution, Tollens' reagent** and **acidified dichromate solution** are all oxidising agents that can be used to distinguish an aldehyde from a ketone.
    (b) When an aldehyde is present the following changes would be observed.
         (1) **Blue** copper(II) ions in **Fehling's solution** are reduced to form an **orange-red precipitate** involving copper(I) ions;
         (2) **Tollens' reagent** forms a layer of **silver** metal on the inside of the glass container ('silver mirror' test); and
         (3) **Acidified dichromate solution** changes from an **orange** colour to a **blue green** colour.

6. (a) ethanol

    (b)
    $$CH_3-\overset{\overset{\displaystyle H}{|}}{C}=O$$

7. (a) **A**

$$CH_3-\underset{\underset{H}{|}}{\overset{\overset{OH}{|}}{C}}-CH_3$$

B

$$CH_3-\overset{\overset{O}{\|}}{C}-CH_3$$

[The alcohol must be a
secondary alcohol as the
oxidation produces a ketone.]

(b) The formation of a ketone from a secondary alcohol is an **oxidation**.

8. (a)

$$CH_3-CH_2-\underset{\underset{CH_3}{|}}{CH}-\overset{\overset{H}{|}}{C}=O$$

$$CH_3-CH_2-\underset{\underset{CH_3}{|}}{CH}-C\overset{\nearrow O}{\underset{\searrow OH}{}}$$

(b)   2-methylbutanal   2-methylbutanoic acid

9.   When an alcohol is oxidised to an aldehyde, the **oxygen to hydrogen ratio increases** as the number of oxygen atoms in the molecule remains the same, but the number of hydrogen atoms decreases by two.
       When an aldehyde is oxidised to a carboxylic acid, the **oxygen to hydrogen ratio increases** as the number of oxygen atoms in the molecule increases by one, but the number of hydrogen atoms remains the same.

10. (a) **X**

$$CH_3-CH_2-\underset{\underset{H}{|}}{\overset{\overset{OH}{|}}{C}}-CH_3$$

Y

$$CH_3-CH_2-\overset{\overset{O}{\|}}{C}-CH_3$$

[Alcohol **X** must be a
secondary alcohol as the
oxidation produces a ketone.]

[**Y** must be a ketone as it does not
oxidise, and it must have the formula
C_4H_8O to give molecular mass 72.]

(b) Alcohol **X** is **butan-2-ol**.
(c) **X** is a **secondary alcohol**. [See above note.]

11. (a)

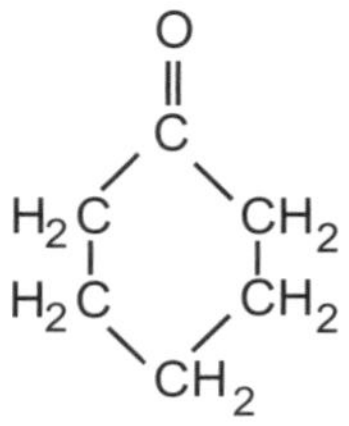

cyclohexanone

(b) **Cyclohexanol** (compound **A**) forms cyclohexanone on oxidation.

12. (a) Oxidation
(b) Catalytic dehydrogenation would not occur as methylpropan-2-ol is a **tertiary alcohol** which **does not undergo oxidation**.

13. (a)

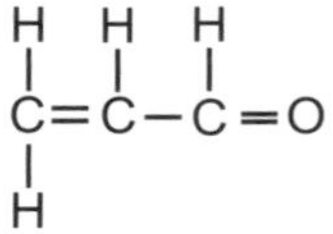

(b) Reaction **B** can be classified as reduction as it involves the **oxygen to hydrogen ratio decreasing,** as the number of oxygen atoms in the molecule remains the same, but the number of hydrogen atoms increases by two.

(c)

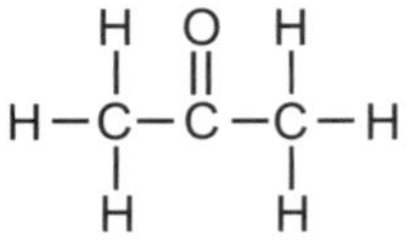

propanone

[Ketones are not oxidised with Fehling's solution, Tollens' reagent or acidified dichromate solution.]

14. (a) i)

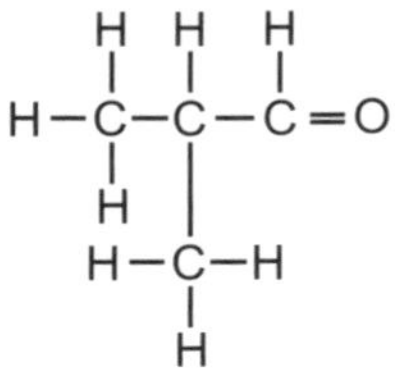

ii)

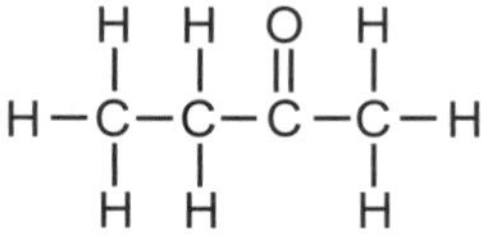

(b) oxidation
(c) Fehling's solution, Tollens' reagent and acidified dichromate solution would all be able to convert butanal to compound **X**.
[Compound **X** is butanoic acid.]

Miscellaneous reactions

1. **A** $CH_2{=}CH_2$

    B $CH_3{-}\overset{\displaystyle O}{\overset{\|}{C}}{-}CH_3$

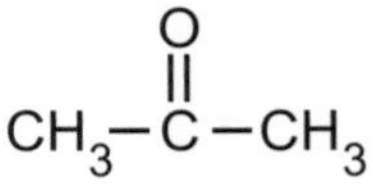

    C $CH_3{-}CH_2{-}\overset{\displaystyle O}{\overset{\diagup\!\!\diagdown}{C}}{-}OH$

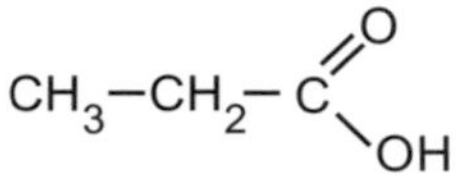

2. (a) a ketone

    (b) i) $CH_3{-}CH{=}\overset{\displaystyle CH_3}{\overset{\|}{C}}{-}CH_3$

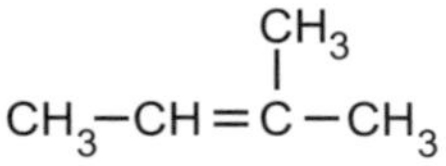

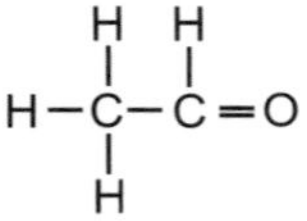

    ii) $CH_3{-}\overset{\displaystyle CH_3}{\underset{\displaystyle H}{C}}{-}\overset{\displaystyle Cl}{\underset{\displaystyle H}{C}}{-}\overset{\displaystyle Cl}{\underset{\displaystyle H}{C}}{-}H$

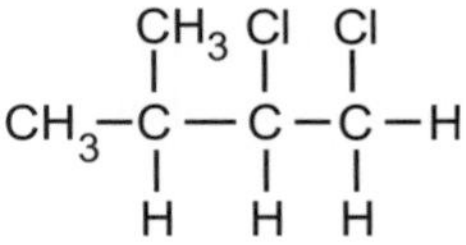

3. (a) i) **A** $H{-}\overset{\displaystyle H}{\underset{\displaystyle H}{C}}{-}\overset{\displaystyle H}{C}{=}O$

    B $H{-}\overset{\displaystyle H}{\underset{\displaystyle H}{C}}{-}\overset{\diagup\!\!\diagdown}{C}{-}OH$ (with $=O$)

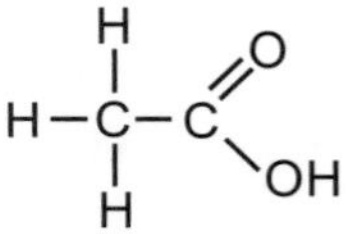

    ii) Fehling's solution, Tollens' reagent and acidified dichromate solution are able to oxidise **A** to produce **B**.

    (b) Step 1 reagent is **hydrogen bromide**.
    Step 2 reagent is **hydrogen**.

4. (a) i) The liquid is **unsaturated**. [no carbon to carbon double bonds]
       ii) The liquid is a **ketone**.

    (b) propanone

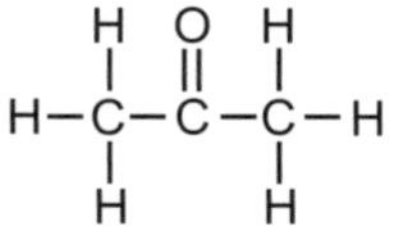

    $H{-}\overset{\displaystyle H}{\underset{\displaystyle H}{C}}{-}\overset{\displaystyle O}{\overset{\|}{C}}{-}\overset{\displaystyle H}{\underset{\displaystyle H}{C}}{-}H$

5. Step 1

$$CH_3-CH_2=CH_2 \quad \rightarrow \quad CH_3-\underset{\underset{H}{|}}{\overset{\overset{OH}{|}}{C}}-CH_3$$

The reagent used in step 1 is **water** (steam).

Step 2

$$CH_3-\underset{\underset{H}{|}}{\overset{\overset{OH}{|}}{C}}-CH_3 \quad \rightarrow \quad CH_3-\overset{\overset{O}{\|}}{C}-CH_3$$

The reagent used in step 2 is either **acidified dichromate solution** or **hot copper(II) oxide**.

6. (a) **P** is **propan-1-ol** and **Q** is **propan-2-ol**.
    (b) **R**

$$CH_3-CH_2-\overset{\overset{H}{|}}{C}=O$$

    (c) the **carboxyl** group (–COOH) and the **amino** (or amine) group ($-NH_2$)
    (d) Step 1 is **dehydration**; step 2 is **oxidation**.

7. (a) i)
       (I) butan-1-ol   (II)   butan-2-ol
       (III) methylpropan-2-ol   (IV)   methylpropan-1-ol
       ii)
       (I) and (IV) – primary alcohols   (II) – secondary alcohol
       (III) – tertiary alcohol.
    (b) i) **D** is alcohol (III). It is the only tertiary alcohol and tertiary alcohols are not oxidised by acidified potassium dichromate solution.
       ii) **C** is alcohol (II). Alcohols (I) and (IV) are both primary alcohols and on complete oxidation with acidified potassium dichromate solution give acids of formula C_3H_7COOH.
       Alcohol (II) is a secondary alcohol and will oxidise to form a ketone, but will not oxidise further.
       iii) On dehydration only alcohols with a branched chain,
       i.e. (III) and (IV), can produce alkenes with branched chains.
       As alcohol (III) is known to be **D**, alcohol (IV) must be **A** – the only remaining alcohol with a branched chain, as **A** and **D** produce the same alkene.
       Therefore, **A** is alcohol (IV) and by elimination **B** is alcohol (I).

8. (a) i)

$$CH_3-CH_2 \diagdown \quad \diagup H$$
$$C=C$$
$$H \diagup \quad \diagdown H$$

ii) but-1-ene

$$CH_3 \diagdown \quad \diagup CH_3$$
$$C=C$$
$$H \diagup \quad \diagdown H$$

but-2-ene

$$H \diagdown \quad \diagup CH_3$$
$$C=C$$
$$H \diagup \quad \diagdown CH_3$$

methylpropene

(b) i) an **orange-red precipitate** would be seen to give a positive result in the Benedict's test.

ii) **Y** is an **aldehyde** and **Z** is a **ketone**.

iii) methylpropene

[Methylpropene is the only alkene of the three that would give both an aldehyde and a ketone on ozonolysis; the other 2 would both produce aldehydes only, in which case **Y** and **Z** would both give a positive Benedict's test.]

(c) i)

$$H_2C-CH_2$$
$$\ | \quad \ |$$
$$H_2C-CH_2$$

ii) cyclobutane

iii) Test with bromine solution.
This isomer (cyclobutane) would **not** readily decolourise the solution.

9. (a) A secondary alcohol

(b) Compound **2**   Compound **3**

$$CH_3-CH=CH-CH_3$$ $$CH_3-CH_2-CH=CH_2$$

(c) Both step **A** reactions are **dehydration** reactions.
Both step **B** reactions are **addition** reactions.

(d) Either **acidified dichromate solution** or **hot copper(II) oxide** could be used in step **D**.
Fehling's solution, Tollens' reagent and acidified dichromate solution could be used in step **E**.

(e) Compound **8**   Compound **9**

$$CH_3-CH_2-\overset{\overset{\displaystyle O}{||}}{C}-CH_3$$ $$CH_3-CH_2-CH_2-\overset{\overset{\displaystyle H}{|}}{C}=O$$

(f) Compound **7** is an isomer of compound **1**.
[Compound **6** is **not** an isomer because it is the same compound as compound **1**.]

Everyday chemistry

1. (a) **Eugenol** is more likely to be soluble in fats and oils.
    (b) Eugenol has fewer polar groups than vanillin and so will be less soluble in water and more soluble in fats and oils.

2. (a) i) A volatile compound is one that will evaporate easily.
        Ii) Limonene will evaporate more easily than squalene because it has smaller molecular mass.
    (b) Limonene has no polar groups and is therefore more likely to be soluble in oils which are also mainly non-polar compounds.

3. (a) **Acetone** is a better solvent for camphor than water.
    (b) Camphor is a mainly non-polar compound. Therefore, it is likely to be more soluble in non-polar acetone than in polar water.

4.   Fructose is a polar molecule due to the –OH groups in its structure.
        It will therefore be soluble in polar water with which it can form hydrogen bonds.

5. (a) **Asparagus** should be cooked in oils/butter to retain the flavour.
    (b) 'Flavour compounds' with polar groups in their molecules are likely to be soluble in polar water. Oils/butter contain mainly non-polar molecules and therefore the 'flavour molecules' do not dissolve into the cooking medium and flavour is retained.

6. (a) An essential oil carries the distinctive aroma of the plant from which is was obtained.
    (b)

Peel	Berry	Leaf	Flower
grapefruit	juniper	basil	lavender
lemon		eucalyptus	rose
orange		thyme	
		wintergreen	

7. (a) **Terpenes** are the family of carbon compounds formed by the joining of isoprene units.
    (b) The two terms to describe the structure of isoprene are **hydrocarbon** and **unsaturated**.

8. (a) Selinene will decolourise bromine solution.

   (b) i)

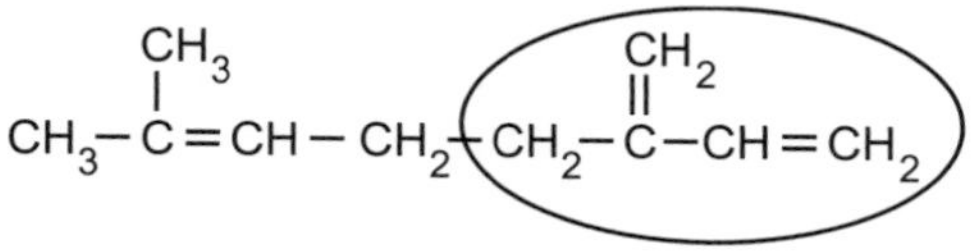

$$CH_3-\underset{\underset{CH_3}{|}}{C}=CH-CH_2-CH_2-\underset{\underset{\|}{CH_2}}{C}-CH=CH_2$$

   ii) **Three** isoprene units are used in making one selinene molecule.
   [Isoprene has 5 carbon atoms; selinene has 15 carbon atoms.]

9.   Any two of the following can result in the deterioration of food quality from the oxidation of food molecules.
   • Loss of colour
   • Reduction of flavour
   • Decrease in nutritional value
   • Health risks from the products of the oxidation

10. (a) Crisps are packaged in nitrogen to prevent oxidation.
   [No oxygen is present, and nitrogen is very unreactive.]
   (b) Cucumbers are wrapped in cellophane or coated in wax to keep out oxygen and prevent oxidation.

11. (a) Antioxidants are substances that inhibit the oxidation of molecules in food.
   (b) Antioxidants in food inhibit oxidation of molecules in food, and as a result preserve quality and extend shelf-life.
   (c) Antioxidants are reducing agents and therefore they themselves are oxidised in any reaction that takes place.

Free radicals

1. (a) Free radicals are atoms or groups of atoms with one or more unpaired electrons.

    [e.g. a chlorine atom $Cl^{\bullet}$ or a methyl group $CH_3^{\bullet}$, where the dot $^{\bullet}$ represents the unpaired electron.]

    (b) The formation of free radicals is as a result of molecules gaining sufficient energy for bonds to be broken. The ultraviolet (UV) radiation from the sun in the atmosphere is a high energy form of light that can bring about this change.

2. (a) Photoaging is caused by long term exposure to UV light. The UV light promotes the formation of free radicals that damage the skin.

    (b) Sun-block products limit damage to skin by producing a barrier to UV radiation.

3. (a) A free radical scavenger is a very reactive molecule that 'mops up' other free radicals to form stable molecules and thus prevent damaging reactions.

    (b) Different forms of Vitamin E occur naturally. All act as free radical scavengers that help to prevent free radical damage to cells in the body.

4. (a) A free radical chain reaction is one that continues because for every free radical that is produced at the beginning, a similar new free radical is generated at the end.

    (b) i) The three steps that occur in a free radical chain reaction are **initiation**, **propagation** and **termination**.

    ii) In the **initiation** step, the chain is started by UV light breaking covalent bonds to form free radicals.

    In the **propagation** step, a reacting free radical is also a product of the reaction, and keeps the chain reaction going.

    In the **termination** step, free radicals are removed when two collide and join together without producing any new free radicals and so the chain reaction eventually stops.

5.

Initiation step(s)	Propagation step(s)	Termination step(s)
A	B C	D E F

6. (a) $Cl_2 \rightarrow Cl^\bullet + Cl^\bullet$

(b) $H^\bullet + Cl_2 \rightarrow HCl + Cl^\bullet$

(c) Any one of the following:

$Cl^\bullet + Cl^\bullet \rightarrow Cl_2$

$H^\bullet + H^\bullet \rightarrow H_2$

$H^\bullet + Cl^\bullet \rightarrow HCl$

Problem solving: patterns in carbon compounds

1. (a)

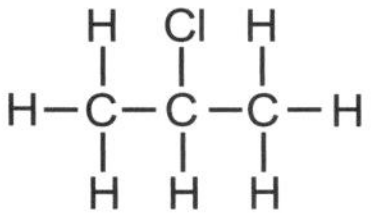

```
    H  Cl H
    |  |  |
H − C− C − C − H
    |  |  |
    H  H  H
```

   (b) When hydrogen chloride reacts with but-2-ene in an addition reaction it is not necessary to consider Markovnikoff's rule as both carbon atoms of the double bond have the same number of attached hydrogen atoms.

2. (a) propene, ethanoic acid

   (b)

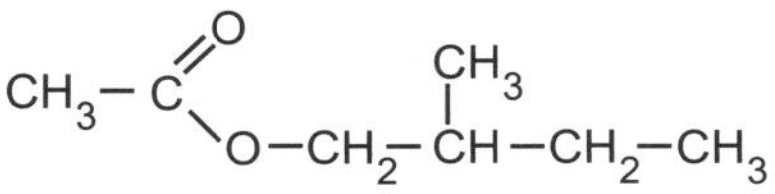

```
            O
           //
CH₃ − C             CH₃
          \          |
           O−CH₂− CH −CH₂−CH₃
```

   (c) The formation of the alkene during pyrolysis involves the removal of a hydrogen atom to form the alkene. When this hydrogen atom is removed the double bond can be formed in different ways.

   (d) methyl ethanoate

3. (a) i)

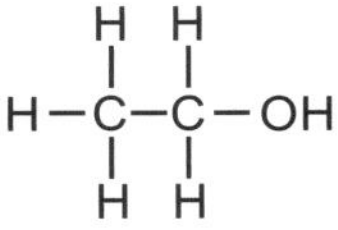

```
    H H
    | |
H − C−C − OH
    | |
    H H
```

   ii) 2-methylpropan-2-ol
   iii) 2-methylbutan-2-ol

   (b) hydration

4.

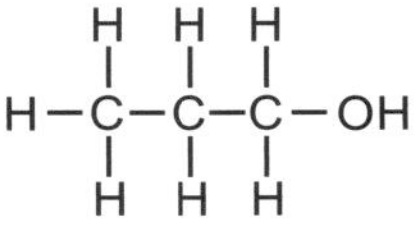

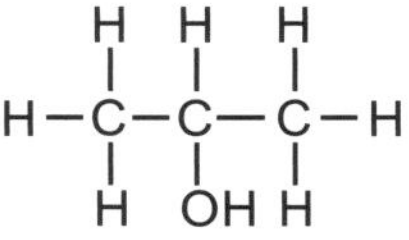

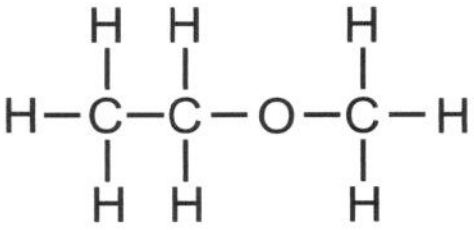

```
    H  H  H
    |  |  |
H − C− C− C − OH
    |  |  |
    H  H  H
```

```
    H  H  H
    |  |  |
H − C− C− C − H
    |  |  |
    H  OH H
```

```
    H H      H
    | |      |
H − C−C − O−C − H
    | |      |
    H H      H
```

5. (a) i) pentan-2-one

   ii) $CH_3-CH_2-CH_2-CH_2-NH_2$

   (b) *The product of Stage 1 should be the reactant in Stage 2.*
   hydrogenation or addition

6. (a) 4-methylpent-2-ene
   (b) Any alkene with an even number of carbons and the C=C double bond in the middle of the chain, e.g. **but-2-ene**, **hex-3-ene**, **oct-4-ene**.

7. (a)

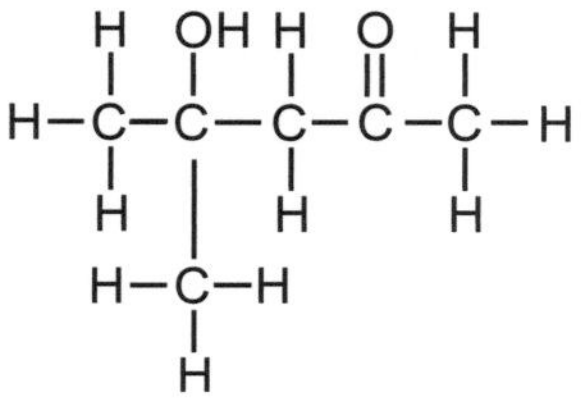

   (b) methanal (or 2,2-dimethylpropanal)
   (c) When molecules join up to form a longer product molecule in a condensation reaction, this is a result of the elimination of atoms to form a small molecule, usually water (hence the name).
   The aldol condensation only produces a larger molecule product with no small molecule product also being produced.

The design of an industrial process

1. (a) A feedstock is a reactant from which other chemicals can be extracted or synthesised.
   (b) Three important factors in deciding which feedstock to use are:
       - **Availability** of the feedstock
       - **Cost** of the feedstock
       - **Sustainability** (and future availability) of the feedstock

2. **Calcium carbonate, water, sodium chloride, oxygen** and **nitrogen** are all relatively cheap and readily available.

3. (a) Sustainability of a feedstock means that it is not going to run out and can continue to be supplied in the long term with minimum effect on the environment.
   (b) **Air** and **water** can be described as being sustainable feedstocks.

4. **Example**: In the production of ammonia by the Haber Process, unreacted nitrogen and hydrogen are recycled.

5. Energy released in exothermic reactions can be used to raise the temperature of reactants to keep down energy costs.

6. A marketable by-product is any additional product of a reaction or process that can be sold to keep down costs.
   Examples: Hydrogen produced as a by-product of cracking ethane to ethene can be sold for use as a fuel or as a reactant in the Haber Process; sulphur removed from crude oil during the distillation process can be sold as a feedstock for the production of sulphuric acid.

7. Increasing the pressure increases the yield of ammonia.
   However, the increase in yield by using pressures in excess of 200 atmospheres is not justified by the greater costs of achieving these higher pressures.

8. Examples of steps taken by the chemical industry to reduce damage to the environment include
   - **reduced levels of discharge of harmful chemicals**
   - **minimising waste** by recycling and use of by-products in other processes
   - **reduced use and production of toxic chemicals**
   - manufacture of **more biodegradable products**

Mole calculations (revision)

1.   **Reminder: M = n x GFM   or   mass = no. of moles x GFM**

(a) GFM of CH_4 = 12 + (4 x 1) = 16 g
     Therefore, M = 10 x 16 = **160 g**
(b) GFM of SO_2 = 32.1 + (2 x 16) = 64.1 g
     Therefore, M = 0.5 x 64.1 = **32.05 g**
(c) GFM of $CaCO_3$ = 40.1 + 12 + (3 x 16) = 100.1 g
     Therefore, M = 2 x 100.1 = **200.2 g**
(d) GFM of $(NH_4)_2Cr_2O_7$ = (2 x 14) + (8 x 1) + (2 x 52) + (7 x 16) = 252 g
     Therefore, M = 0.1 x 252 = **25.2 g**

2.   **Reminder: n = $\dfrac{M}{GFM}$ or   no. of moles = mass ÷ GFM**

(a) GFM of C_2H_4 = (2 x12) + (4 x 1) = 28 g
     Therefore, n = 14 ÷ 28 = **0.5 mol**
(b) GFM of KNO_3 = 39.1 + 14 + (3 x 16) = 101.1 g
     Therefore, n = 202.2 ÷ 101.1 = **2 mol**
(c) GFM of Na_2CO_3 = (2 x 23) + 12 + (3 x 16) = 106 g
     Therefore, n = 10.6 ÷ 106 = **0.1 mol**
(d) GFM of $(NH_4)_2SO_4$ = (2 x 14) + (8 x 1) + 32.1 + (4 x 16) = 132.1 g
     Therefore, n = 2642 ÷ 132.1 = **20 mol**

3.   **Reminder: n = C x V   or   no. of moles = conc. x litres**

(a) n = 1 x 0.2 = **0.2 mol**
(b) n = 0.5 x 0.5 = **0.25 mol**
(c) n = 2 x 0.1 = **0.2 mol**
(d) n = 0.2 x 2 = **0.4 mol**

4.   **Reminder: C = $\dfrac{n}{V}$ or   conc. = no. of moles ÷ litres**

(a) C = 1 ÷ 0.5 = **2 mol l^{-1}**
(b) C = 2 ÷ 0.2 = **10 mol l^{-1}**
(c) C = 0.5 ÷ 0.25 = **2 mol l^{-1}**
(d) C = 0.1 ÷ 1 = **0.1 mol l^{-1}**

5.   Reminder: V = $\frac{n}{c}$ or litres = no. of moles ÷ concentration

(a) V = 2 ÷ 1 = **2 litres**
(b) V = 0.4 ÷ 2 = **0.2 litres or 200 cm^3**
(c) V = 0.1 ÷ 0.2 = **0.5 litres or 500 cm^3**
(d) V = 0.2 ÷ 1 = **0.2 litres or 200 cm^3**

6.   Reminder 1: n = C x V or no. of moles = conc. x litres
Reminder 2: M = n x GFM or   mass = no. of moles x GFM

(a) n = C x V = 4 x 0.05 = 0.2 mol
GFM of KCl = 39.1 + 35.5 = 74.6 g
Therefore, M = 0.2 x 74.6 = **14.9 g**
(b) n = C x V = 0.2 x 0.1 = 0.02 mol
GFM of Na_2SO_4 = (2 x 23) + 32.1 + (4 x 16) = 142.1 g
Therefore, M = 0.02 x 142.1 = **2.84 g**
(c) n = C x V = 1 x 0.025 = 0.025 mol
GFM of $Mg(NO_3)_2$ = 24.3 + (2 x 14) + (6 x 16) = 148.3 g
Therefore, M = 0.025 x 148.3 = **3.71 g**
(d) n = C x V = 0.1 x 0.5 = 0.05 mol
GFM of $(NH_4)_2CO_3$ = (2 x 14) + (8 x 1) + 12 + (3 x 16) = 96 g
Therefore, M = 0.05 x 96 = **4.8 g**

7.   Reminder 1: n = $\frac{M}{GFM}$ or no. of moles = Mass ÷ GFM
Reminder 2: C = $\frac{n}{V}$ or   conc. = no. of moles ÷ litres

(a) GFM of NaOH = 23 + 16 + 1 = 40 g
Therefore, n = 4 ÷ 40 = 0.1 mol
Therefore, C = 0.1 ÷ 1 = **0.1 mol l^{-1}**
(b) GFM of K_2CO_3 = (2 x 39.1) + 12 + (3 x 16) = 138.2 g
Therefore, n = 13.82 ÷ 138.2 = 0.1 mol
Therefore, C = 0.1 ÷ 2 = **0.05 mol l^{-1}**
(c) GFM of $CuSO_4$ = 63.5 + 32.1 + (4 x 16) = 159.6 g
Therefore, n = 31.92 ÷ 159.6 = 0.2 mol
Therefore, C = 0.2 ÷ 0.25 = **0.8 mol l^{-1}**
(d) GFM of NH_4NO_3 = 14 + (4 x 1) + 14 + (3 x 16) = 80 g
Therefore, n = 10 ÷ 80 = 0.125 mol
Therefore, C = 0.125 ÷ 0.1 = **1.25 mol l^{-1}**

The Avogadro constant (i)

1. (a)   1 mol of SO_2 contains 1 mol of molecules
Therefore, 0.5 mol of SO_2 contains 0.5 mol of SO_2 molecules
But each SO_2 molecule contains 2 oxygen atoms
Therefore, 0.5 mol of SO_2 contains 2 x 0.5 = **1 mol** of oxygen atoms

    (b)   1 mol of CH_4 contains 1 mol of CH_4 molecules
Therefore, 2 mol of CH_4 contains 2 mol of CH_4 molecules
But each CH_4 molecule contains 4 hydrogen atoms
Therefore, 2 mol of CH_4 contains 4 x 2 mol = **8 mol** of hydrogen atoms

    (c)   1 mol of C_4H_{10} contains 1 mol of C_4H_{10} molecules
Therefore, 4 mol of C_4H_{10} contains 4 mol of C_4H_{10} molecules
But each C_4H_{10} molecule contains 4 carbon atoms
Therefore, 4 mol of C_4H_{10} contains 4 x 4 = **16 mol** of carbon atoms

    (d)   1 mol of NH_3 contains 1 mol of NH_3 molecules
Therefore, 0.2 mol of NH_3 contains 0.2 mol of NH_3 molecules
But each NH_3 molecule contains 4 atoms
Therefore, 0.2 mol of NH_3 contains 4 x 0.2 = **0.8 mol** of atoms

    (e)   1 mol of C_2H_5OH contains 1 mol of C_2H_5OH molecules
Therefore, 10 mol of C_2H_5OH contains 10 mol of C_2H_5OH molecules
But each C_2H_5OH molecule contains 9 atoms
Therefore, 10 mol of C_2H_5OH contains 9 x 10 atoms = **90 mol** of atoms

2. (a)   1 mol of Mg_3N_2 contains 1 mol of Mg_3N_2 formula units
But each Mg_3N_2 formula unit contains 3 mol of Mg^{2+} ions
Therefore, 1 mol of Mg_3N_2 contains 3 x 1 = **3 mol** of Mg^{2+} ions

    (b)   1 mol of Na_2O contains 1 mol of Na_2O formula units
Therefore, 0.05 mol of Na_2O contains 0.05 mol of Na_2O formula units
But each Na_2O formula unit contains 2 Na^+ ions
Therefore, 0.05 mol of Na_2O contains 2 x 0.05 = **0.1 mol** of Na^+ ions

2. (c) 1 mol of $Ca(OH)_2$ contains 1 mol of $Ca(OH)_2$ formula units
Therefore, 0.1 mol of $Ca(OH)_2$ contains 0.1 mol of $Ca(OH)_2$ formula units
But each $Ca(OH)_2$ formula unit contains 2 OH^- (hydroxide) ions
Therefore, 0.1 mol of $Ca(OH)_2$ contains 2 x 0.1 =
0.2 mol of OH^- (hydroxide) ions

(d) 1 mol of $CuSO_4$ contains 1 mol of $CuSO_4$ formula units
Therefore, 5 mol of $CuSO_4$ contains 5 mol of $CuSO_4$ formula units
But each $CuSO_4$ formula unit contains 2 ions [1 Cu^{2+} and 1 SO_4^{2-}]
Therefore, 5 mol of $CuSO_4$ contains 2 x 5 = **10 mol** of ions

(e) 1 mol of NH_4Cl contains 1 mol of NH_4Cl formula units
Therefore, 0.4 mol of NH_4Cl contains 0.4 mol of NH_4Cl formula units
But each NH_4Cl formula unit contains 2 ions [1 NH_4^+ and 1 Cl^-]
Therefore, 0.4 mol of NH_4Cl contains 2 x 0.4 = **0.8 mol** of ions

3. (a) 6 g of magnesium = 6 ÷ 24.3 = 0.247 mol
6 g of calcium = 6 ÷ 40.1 = 0.150 mol
Therefore, **magnesium** contains more atoms

(b) 3 g of sodium = 3 ÷ 23 = 0.130 mol
5 g of potassium = 5 ÷ 39.1 = 0.128 mol
Therefore, **sodium** contains more atoms

(c) 2 g of helium = 2 ÷ 4 = 0.5 mol
10 g of argon = 10 ÷ 39.9 = 0.251 mol
Therefore, **helium** contains more atoms

(d) 20 g of water (H_2O) = 20 ÷ 18 = 1.11 mol
20 g of carbon dioxide (CO_2) = 20 ÷ 44 = 0.455 mol
Therefore, **water** contains more molecules

(e) 10 g of ammonia (NH_3) = 10 ÷ 17 = 0.588 mol
16 g of oxygen (O_2) = 16 ÷ 32 = 0.5 mol
Therefore, **ammonia** contains more molecules

(f) 100 g of methane (CH_4) = 100 ÷ 16 = 6.25 mol
50 g of ethane (C_2H_6) = 50 ÷ 30 = 1.67 mol
Therefore, **methane** contains more molecules

3. (g) 1 g of lithium chloride (Li^+Cl^-) = 1 ÷ (6.9 + 35.5) = 0.0236 mol
1 g of potassium chloride (K^+Cl^-) = 1 ÷ (39.1 + 35.5) = 0.0134 mol
Since 1 formula unit of both substances contains 2 ions
lithium chloride contains more ions

(h) 10 g of magnesium sulphide ($Mg^{2+}S^{2-}$) = 10 ÷ (24.3 + 32.1) = 0.177 mol
2 g of calcium oxide ($Ca^{2+}O^{2-}$) = 2 ÷ (40.1 + 16) = 0.036 mol
Since 1 formula unit of both substances contains 2 ions
magnesium sulphide contains more ions

(i) 80 g of sodium hydroxide (Na^+OH^-) = 80 ÷ (23.1 +16 + 1) = 1.995 mol
but 2 mol of ions in each mol, therefore 2 x 1.995 = 3.99 mol of ions
200 g of sodium sulphate [$(Na^+)_2SO_4^{2-}$]
= 200 ÷ ((2 x 23.1) + 32.1 + (4 x 16)) = 200 ÷ 142.3 = 1.405 mol
but 3 mol of ions in each mol, therefore 3 x 1.405 = 4.215 mol of ions
Therefore, **sodium sulphate** contains more ions

(j) 40 g of neon (Ne) = 40 ÷ 20.2 = 1.980 mol
60 g of sulphur dioxide (SO_2) = 60 ÷ (32.1 + (2 x 16)) = 0.936 mol
but each molecule of SO_2 contains 3 atoms,
therefore, 3 x 0.936 = 2.808 mol of atoms
Therefore, **sulphur dioxide** contains more atom

(k) 1 g of hydrogen (H_2) = 1 ÷ 2 = 0.5 mol
but each molecule of H_2 contains 2 atoms,
therefore, 2 x 0.5 = 1 mol of atoms
50 g of carbon tetrachloride (CCl_4) = 50 ÷ (12 + (4 x 35.5)) = 0.352 mol
but each molecule of CCl_4 contains 5 atoms,
therefore, 5 x 0.352 = 1.76 mol of atoms
Therefore, **carbon tetrachloride** contains more atoms

(l) 80 g of hydrogen chloride (HCl) = 80 ÷ (1 + 35.5) = 2.19 mol
but each molecule of HCl contains 2 atoms,
therefore, 2 x 2.19 = 4.38 mol of atoms
10 g of propene (C_3H_6) = 10 ÷ ((3 x 12) + (6 x 1)) = 0.238 mol
but each molecule of C_3H_6 contains 9 atoms,
therefore, 9 x 0.238 = 2.142 mol of atoms
Therefore, **hydrogen chloride** contains more atoms

The Avogadro constant (ii)

1. (a) 1 mol of sulphur has a mass of 32.1 g and contains 6.02×10^{23} atoms
    Therefore, 160.5 g contains $(160.5 \div 32.1) \times 6.02 \times 10^{23}$ atoms =
    3.01×10^{24} atoms

    (b) 1 mol of calcium has a mass of 40.1 g and contains 6.02×10^{23} atoms
    Therefore, 401 g contains $(401 \div 40.1) \times 6.02 \times 10^{23}$ atoms =
    6.02×10^{24} atoms

    (c) 1 mol of carbon-14 has a mass of 14 g and contains 6.02×10^{23} atoms
    Therefore, 0.0014 g contains $(0.0014 \div 14) \times 6.02 \times 10^{23}$ atoms =
    6.02×10^{19} atoms

    (d) 1 mol of sodium has a mass of 23 g and contains 6.02×10^{23} atoms
    Therefore, 46 kg contains $1000 \times (46 \div 23) \times 6.02 \times 10^{23}$ atoms =
    1.204×10^{27} atoms

2. (a) 1 mol of CO_2 has a mass of 44 g and contains 6.02×10^{23} molecules
    Therefore, 1.1 g contains $(1.1 \div 44) \times 6.02 \times 10^{23}$ molecules =
    1.505×10^{22} molecules

    (b) 1 mol of H_2O has a mass of 18 g and contains 6.02×10^{23} molecules
    Therefore, 90 g contains $(90 \div 18) \times 6.02 \times 10^{23}$ molecules =
    3.01×10^{24} molecules

    (c) 1 mol of CH_4 has a mass of 16 g and contains 6.02×10^{23} molecules
    Therefore, 3.2 g contains $(3.2 \div 16) \times 6.02 \times 10^{23}$ molecules =
    1.204×10^{23} molecules

    (d) 1 mol of $C_{12}H_{22}O_{11}$ has a mass of $[(12 \times 12) + (22 \times 1) + (11 \times 16)] =$
    342 g and contains 6.02×10^{23} molecules
    Therefore, 3.42 g contains $(3.42 \div 342) \times 6.02 \times 10^{23}$ molecules =
    6.02×10^{21} molecules

3. (a) 1 mol of KF has a mass of (39.1 + 19) = 58.1 g
        and contains 6.02×10^{23} formula units
        Therefore, 5.81 g contains $(5.81 \div 58.1) \times 6.02 \times 10^{23}$ formula units =
        6.01×10^{22} formula units

    (b) 1 mol of CaO has a mass of (40.1 + 16) = 56.1 g
        and contains 6.02×10^{23} formula units
        Therefore, 561 g contains $(561 \div 56.1) \times 6.02 \times 10^{23}$ formula units =
        6.01×10^{24} formula units

    (c) 1 mol of $CuCl_2$ has a mass of [63.5 + (2 x 35.5)] = 134.5 g
        and contains 6.02×10^{23} formula units
        Therefore, 269 g contains $(269 \div 134.5) \times 6.02 \times 10^{23}$ formula units =
        1.204×10^{24} formula units

    (d) 1 mol of NaOH has a mass of (23 + 16 + 1) = 40 g
        and contains 6.02×10^{23} formula units
        Therefore, 1 kg contains $(1000 \div 40) \times 6.02 \times 10^{23}$ formula units =
        1.505×10^{25} formula units

4. (a) 1 mol of H_2O has a mass of 18 g and contains 6.02×10^{23} molecules
        But each molecule contains 3 atoms
        Therefore, 1.8 g contains $3 \times (1.8 \div 18) \times 6.02 \times 10^{23}$ atoms =
        1.806×10^{23} atoms

    (b) 1 mol of C_6H_{14} has a mass of 86 g and contains 6.02×10^{23} molecules
        But each molecule contains 20 atoms
        Therefore, 8.6 g contains $20 \times (8.6 \div 86) \times 6.02 \times 10^{23}$ atoms =
        1.204×10^{24} atoms

    (c) 1 mol of NH_3 has a mass of 17 g and contains 6.02×10^{23} molecules
        But each molecule contains 4 atoms
        Therefore, 3.4 g contains $4 \times (3.4 \div 17) \times 6.02 \times 10^{23}$ atoms =
        4.816×10^{23} atoms

    (d) 1 mol of C_2H_5OH has a mass of 46 g and contains 6.02×10^{23} molecules
        But each molecule contains 9 atoms
        Therefore, 9.2 g contains $9 \times (9.2 \div 46) \times 6.02 \times 10^{23}$ atoms =
        1.084×10^{24} atoms

5. (a) 1 mol of K_2O has a mass of $[(2 \times 39.1) + 16)] = 94.2$ g
and contains 6.02×10^{23} formula units
But each formula unit contains 3 ions (2 K^+ and 1 O^{2-})
Therefore, 9.42 g contains $3 \times (9.42 \div 94.2) \times 6.02 \times 10^{23}$ ions =
1.806 x 10²³ ions

(b) 1 mol of $Ca(OH)_2$ has a mass of $[40.1 + (2 \times 16) + (2 \times 1)] = 74.1$ g
and contains 6.02×10^{23} formula units
But each formula unit contains 3 ions (1 Ca^{2+} and 2 OH$^-$)
Therefore, 1482 g contains $3 \times (1482 \div 74.1) \times 6.02 \times 10^{23}$ ions =
3.612 x 10²⁵ ions

(c) 1 mol of NaCl has a mass of $(23 + 35.5) = 58.5$ g
and contains 6.02×10^{23} formula units
But each formula unit contains 2 ions (1 Na^+ and 1 Cl$^-$)
Therefore, 585 g contains $2 \times (585 \div 58.5) \times 6.02 \times 10^{23}$ ions =
1.204 x 10²⁵ ions

(d) 1 mol of $Al_2(SO_4)_3$ has a mass of $(2 \times 27)+(3 \times 32.1)+(12 \times 16) = 342.3$ g
and contains 6.02×10^{23} formula units
But each formula unit contains 5 ions (2 Al^{3+} and 3 SO_4^{2-})
Therefore, 34.23 kg contains $5 \times (34230 \div 342.3) \times 6.02 \times 10^{23}$ ions =
3.01 x 10²⁶ ions

6.   1 Al atom → 1 Al^{3+} ion and 3 electrons
Therefore, 1 mol of Al loses 3 mol of electrons
$= 3 \times 6.02 \times 10^{23}$ electrons = **1.806 x 10²⁴ electrons**

Molar volume of gases

> **Reminder:** Molar volume of a gas is the volume occupied by 1 mol of the gas at the stated temperature and pressure.

1. (a) 1 mol of argon (Ar) has a mass of 39.9 g and a volume of 22.4 litres
   Therefore, 2 litres of argon has a mass of $(2 \div 22.4) \times 39.9$ g = **3.56 g**

   (b) 1 mol of methane (CH_4) has a mass of 16 g and a volume of 22.4 litres
   Therefore, 0.1 litres of methane has a mass of $(0.1 \div 22.4) \times 16$ g = **0.0714 g**

   (c) 1 mol of chlorine (Cl_2) has a mass of 71 g and a volume of 22.4 litres
   Therefore, 5 litres of chlorine has a mass of $(5 \div 22.4) \times 71$ g = **15.85 g**

   (d) 1 mol of carbon dioxide (CO_2) has a mass of 44 g and a volume of 22.4 litres
   Therefore, 10 litres of carbon dioxide has a mass of $(10 \div 22.4) \times 44$ g =
   19.64 g

   (e) 1 mol of oxygen (O_2) has a mass of 32 g and a volume of 22.4 litres
   Therefore, 0.5 litres of oxygen has a mass of $(0.5 \div 22.4) \times 32$ g = **0.714 g**

2. (a) 1 mol of ethane (C_2H_6) has a mass of 30 g and a volume of 24.0 litres
   Therefore, 0.3 g of ethane has a volume of $(0.3 \div 30) \times 24$ =
   0.24 litres (or 240 cm^3)

   (b) 1 mol of sulphur dioxide (SO_2) has a mass of 64.1 g and a volume of 24.0 litres
   Therefore, 0.641 g of sulphur dioxide has a volume of
   $(0.641 \div 64.1) \times 24.0$ = **0.24 litres** or (240 cm^3)

   (c) 1 mol of neon (Ne) has a mass of 20.2 g and a volume of 24.0 litres
   Therefore, 4.04 g of neon has a volume of $(4.04 \div 20.2) \times 24.0$ =
   4.8 litres (or 4800 cm^3)

   (d) 1 mol of fluorine (F_2) has a mass of 38 g and a volume of 24.0 litres
   Therefore, 0.76 g of fluorine has a volume of $(0.76 \div 38) \times 24.0$ =
   0.48 litres (or 480 cm^3)

   (e) 1 mol of ammonia (NH_3) has a mass of 17 g and a volume of 24.0 litres
   Therefore, 6.8 kg (6800g) of ammonia has a volume of
   $(6800 \div 17) \times 24.0$ = **9600 litres**

Chemistry in Society

3. (a) 0.226 mol of butane has a volume of 5 litres
Therefore, molar volume of butane is $(1 \div 0.226) \times 5$ = **22.12 litres**

(b) 1.12×10^{-2} mol of sulphur dioxide has a volume of 250 cm^3
Therefore, molar volume of sulphur dioxide is
$(1 \div 1.12 \times 10^{-2}) \times 250 = 22\ 321\ cm^3$ (or **22.32 litres**)

(c) 1 mol of ammonia (NH_3) has a mass of 17 g
Therefore, 0.38 g = $(0.38 \div 17)$ mol, with a volume of 500 cm^3
Therefore, molar volume of ammonia is
$[\ 1 \div (0.38 \div 17)\ ] \times 500 = 22\ 368\ cm^3$ (or **22.37 litres**)

(d) 1 mol of helium (He) has a mass of 4 g
Therefore, 1.8×10^{-2} g = $(1.8 \times 10^{-2} \div 4)$ mol, with a volume of 100 cm^3
Therefore, molar volume of helium is
$[\ 1 \div (1.8 \times 10^{-2} \div 4)\ ] \times 100 = 22\ 222\ cm^3$ = (or **22.22 litres**)

(e) 1 mol of hydrogen (H_2) has a mass of 2 g
Therefore, 0.174 g = $(0.174 \div 2)$ mol, with a volume of 2 litres
Therefore, molar volume of hydrogen is
$[\ 1 \div (0.174 \div 2)\ ] \times 2$ = **22.99 litres**

4. Mass of carbon dioxide in flask = $(368.28 - 367.30) = 0.98$ g
1 mol of carbon dioxide (CO_2) has a mass of 44 g
Therefore, 0.78 g = $(0.98 \div 44)$ mol, with a volume of 500 cm^3
Therefore, molar volume of carbon dioxide is
$[\ 1 \div (0.98 \div 44)\ ] \times 500 = 22\ 449\ cm^3$ (or **22.45 litres**)

Calculations based on equations (i) (revision)

1. (a) CH_4 + $2O_2$ → CO_2 + $2H_2O$
   1 mol of CH_4 → 1 mol of CO_2
   16 g of CH_4 → 44 g of CO_2
   Therefore, 4 g of CH_4 → (4 ÷ 16) x 44 = **11 g of CO_2**

   (b) Cu + $2AgNO_3$ → $Cu(NO_3)_2$ + 2Ag
   1 mol of Cu → 2 mol of Ag
   63.5 g of Cu → 215.8 g of Ag
   Therefore, 12.7 g of Cu → (12.7 ÷ 63.5) x 215.8 = **43.16 g of Ag**

   (c) 4Al + $3O_2$ → $2Al_2O_3$
   4 mol of Al → 2 mol of Al_2O_3
   (4 x 27) = 108 g of Al → 2 x [(2 x 27) + (3 x 16)] = 204 g of Al_2O_3
   Therefore, (10.2 ÷ 204) x 108 g of Al → 10.2 g of Al_2O_3 = **5.4 g of Al**

   (d) $2NaHCO_3$ → Na_2CO_3 + H_2O + CO_2
   2 mol of $NaHCO_3$ → 1 mol of CO_2
   2 x [23 + 1 + 12 + (3x16)] = 168 g of $NaHCO_3$ →12 + (2x16) = 44g of CO_2
   Therefore, 4.2 g of $NaHCO_3$ → (4.2 ÷ 168) x 44 = **1.1 g of CO_2**

   (e) $(NH_4)_2SO_4$ + 2NaOH → Na_2SO_4 + $2NH_3$ + $2H_2O$
   1 mol of $(NH_4)_2SO_4$ → 2 mol of NH_3
   (2x14) + (8x1) + 32.1 + (4x16) = 132.1 g of $(NH_4)_2SO_4$
   → 2 x [14 + (3x1)] = 34 g of NH_3
   Therefore, (0.68 ÷ 34) x 132.1 g of $(NH_4)_2SO_4$ → 0.68 g of NH_3
   = **2.642 g of $(NH_4)_2SO_4$**

   (f) C_2H_4 + H_2O → C_2H_5OH
   1 mol of C_2H_4 → 1 mol of C_2H_5OH
   (2x12)+(4x1) = 28 g of C_2H_4 → (2x12)+(5x1) + 16 + 1 = 46 g of C_2H_5OH
   Therefore, 2.8 x 10^3 g of C_2H_4 → (2.8 x 10^3 ÷ 28) x 46 g of C_2H_5OH
   Therefore, 2.8 x 10^3 kg of C_2H_4 → (2.8 x 10^3 ÷ 28) x 46 kg of C_2H_5OH
   = **4600 kg of C_2H_5OH**

   (g) N_2 + $3H_2$ → $2NH_3$
   3 mol of H_2 → 2 mol of NH_3
   Therefore, (3 x 2) = 6 g of H_2 → 2 x [14 + (3 x 1)] = 34 g of NH_3
   Therefore, 6 tonnes of H_2 → **34 tonnes of NH_3**

1. (h) $CH_3CH_2CH_2OH$ → CH_3CH_2COOH
   1 mol of $CH_3CH_2CH_2OH$ → 1 mol of CH_3CH_2COOH
   (3 x 12) + (8 x 1) + 16 = 60 g of $CH_3CH_2CH_2OH$ →
                    (3 x 12) + (6 x 1) + (2 x 16) = 74 g of CH_3CH_2COOH
   Therefore, 60 kg of propan-1-ol → 74 kg of propanoic acid
   Therefore, (1.48 ÷ 74) x 60 kg propan-1-ol → 1.48 kg of propanoic acid
      = **1.2 kg of propan-1-ol**

Reminder 1:   n = C x V or no. of moles = conc. x litres
Reminder 2:   M = n x GFM or mass = no. of moles x GFM

---

2. (a) Zn + H_2SO_4 → $ZnSO_4$ + H_2
   No. of moles of H_2SO_4 = C x V = 1 x 0.025 = 0.025
   1 mol of Zn reacts with 1 mol $ZnSO_4$
   Therefore, 0.025 mol of Zn reacts with 0.025 mol of H_2SO_4
   Mass of Zn reacted = n x GFM = 0.025 x 65.4 = **1.635 g**

   (b) Fe + 2HCl → $FeCl_2$ + H_2
   No. of moles of HCl = C x V = 0.1 x 0.05 = 0.005
   1 mol of Fe reacts with 2 mol HCl
   Therefore, 0.0025 mol of Fe reacts with 0.005 mol of HCl
   Mass of Fe reacted = n x GFM = 0.0025 x 55.8 = **0.1395 g**

   (c) Zn + $CuSO_4$ → $ZnSO_4$ + Cu
   No. of moles of $CuSO_4$ = C x V = 0.5 x 0.05 = 0.025
   1 mol of $CuSO_4$ → 1 mol of Cu
   Therefore, 0.025 mol of $CuSO_4$ → 0.025 mol of Cu
   Mass of Cu produced = n x GFM = 0.025 x 63.5 = **1.588 g**

3.   Mg + 2HCl → $MgCl_2$ + H_2
   No. of moles of HCl = C x V = 0.1 x 0.1 = 0.01
   1 mol of Mg reacts with 2 mol of HCl
   Therefore, 0.005 mol of Mg reacts with 0.01 mol of HCl
   Mass of magnesium reacted = n x GFM = 0.005 x 24.3 = 0.1215 g
   Therefore, mass of magnesium remaining = 12 – 0.1215 = **11.88 g**

4. $CaCO_3$ + 2HCl → $CaCl_2$ + CO_2 + H_2O
   No. of moles of HCl = C x V = 1 x 0.0501 = 0.0501
   2 mol of HCl reacts with 1 mol $CaCO_3$
   Therefore, 0.0501 mol of HCl reacts with 0.02505 mol of $CaCO_3$
   Mass of $CaCO_3$ reacted = n x GFM = 0.02505 x 100.1 = 2.51 g
   The egg shell sample contained **2.51 g** of calcium carbonate

Calculations based on equations (ii)

1. $Zn\ (s)\ +\ 2HCl\ (aq)\ \rightarrow\ ZnCl_2\ (aq)\ +\ H_2\ (g)$
     1 mol of Zn → 1 mol of H_2
     65.4 g of Zn → 23.2 litres of H_2
     Therefore, 6.54 g of Zn → **2.32 litres of H_2**

2. $S\ (s)\ +\ O_2\ (g)\ \rightarrow\ SO_2\ (g)$
     1 mol of S → 1 mol of SO_2
     32.1 g of S → 23.2 litres of SO_2
     Therefore, 6.42 g of S →(6.42 ÷ 32.1) x 23.2 = **4.64 litres of SO_2**

3. $2Ag_2O\ (s)\ \rightarrow\ 4Ag\ (s)\ +\ O_2\ (g)$
     2 mol of Ag_2O → 1 mol of O_2
     2 x [(2 x 107.9) + 16] = 463.6 g of Ag_2O → 23.2 litres of O_2
     Therefore, 46.36 g of Ag_2O → **2.32 litres of O_2**

4. $2H_2\ (g)\ +\ O_2\ (g)\ \rightarrow\ 2H_2O\ (l)$
     2 mol of H_2 → 2 mol of H_2O
     Therefore, 1 mol H_2 → 1 mol of H_2O
     23.2 litres of H_2 → [(2 x 1) + 16] = 18 g of H_2O
     Therefore, 2 litres of H_2 → (2 ÷ 23.2) x 18 g = **1.55 g of H_2O**

5. $2H_2O_2\ (aq)\ \rightarrow\ 2H_2O\ (l)\ +\ O_2\ (g)$
     2 mol of H_2O_2 → 1 mol of O_2
     2 x [(2 x 1) + (2 x 16)] = 68 g of H_2O_2 → 23.2 litres (23 200 cm^3) of O_2
     Therefore, 58 cm^3 of O_2 is produced by (58 ÷ 23200) x 68 g =
                                               0.17 g of H_2O_2

6. $2NaCl\ (aq)\ \rightarrow\ 2Na\ (s)\ +\ Cl_2\ (g)$
     2 mol of NaCl → 1 mol of Cl_2
     2 x (23 + 35.5) = 117 g of NaCl → 23.2 litres of Cl_2
     Therefore, 100 g of NaCl → (100 ÷ 117) x 23.2 l of Cl_2 = 19.83 litres of Cl_2
     Therefore, 100 kg of NaCl → **19 830 litres of Cl_2**

7. $4CuFeS_2\ (s) + 2SiO_2\ (s) + 5O_2\ (g) \rightarrow 2Cu_2S.FeS\ (l) + 2FeSiO_2\ (l) + 4SO_2\ (g)$
     4 mol of $CuFeS_2$ (s) reacts with 5 mol of O_2
     4 x [63.5 + 55.8 + (2 x 32.1)] g of $CuFeS_2$ reacts with 5 x 23.2 litres of O_2
     i.e. 734 g of $CuFeS_2$ reacts with 116 litres of O_2
     Therefore, 1468 g of $CuFeS_2$ reacts with 232 litres of O_2
     Therefore, 1468 kg of $CuFeS_2$ reacts with **232 000 litres of O_2**

8. $C_6H_{14} \rightarrow C_6H_6 + 4H_2$
         1 mol of $C_6H_{14} \rightarrow$ 4 mol of H_2
         [(6 x 12) + (14 x 1)] = 86 g of $C_6H_{14} \rightarrow$ (4 x 23.2) = 92.8 litres of H_2
         Therefore, 1 kg (1000 g) of $C_6H_{14} \rightarrow$ (1000 ÷ 86) x 92.8 = **1079 litres of H_2**

9. $Mg (s) + H_2SO_4 (aq) \rightarrow MgSO_4 (aq) + H_2 (g)$
         No. of moles of H_2SO_4 = C x V = 0.1 x 0.05 = 0.005
         1 mol of $H_2SO_4 \rightarrow$ 1 mol of H_2
         Therefore, 0.005 mol of $H_2SO_4 \rightarrow$ 0.005 mol of H_2 = 0.005 x 23.2 =
                                            0.116 litres of H_2

10. $Zn (s) + 2HCl (aq) \rightarrow ZnCl_2 (aq) + H_2 (g)$
         No. of moles of HCl = C x V = 0.5 x 0.025 = 0.0125
         1 mol of HCl $\rightarrow$ 1 mol of H_2
         Therefore, 0.0125 mol of $H_2SO_4 \rightarrow$ 0.0125 mol of H_2 = 0.0125 x 23.2 =
                                            0.29 litres of H_2

11. $C_3H_8 (g) + 5O_2 (g) \rightarrow 3CO_2 (g) + 4H_2O (l)$ $\Delta H = -2878$ kJ mol^{-1}
         1 mol C_3H_8 = 23.2 litres $\rightarrow$ 2878 kJ
         Therefore, (7.195 ÷ 2878) x 23.2 litres of $C_3H_8 \rightarrow$ 7.195 kJ
                               = **0.058 litres** (or 58 cm^3) of propane is required.

The idea of excess

Reminder 1: The amount of product formed in a chemical reaction is determined by the reactant that is NOT in excess.

Reminder 2: $n = \frac{M}{GFM}$ or no. of moles = mass ÷ GFM

1. $C + O_2 \rightarrow CO_2$

   No. of moles of C = (4 ÷ 12) = 0.33;

   No. of moles of O_2 = (8 ÷ 32) = 0.25

   1 mol of C reacts with 1 mol of O_2

   Therefore, C is in excess (by 0.08 mol) and mass of CO_2 is determined by the no of moles of O_2.

   1 mol of $O_2 \rightarrow$ 1 mol of CO_2

   Therefore, 0.25 mol of $O_2 \rightarrow$ 0.25 mol of CO_2 = 0.25 x [12 + (2 x16)] =

   11 g of CO_2

2. $Fe + S \rightarrow FeS$

   No. of moles of Fe = (27.9 ÷ 55.8) = 0.5;

   No. of moles of S = (3.21 ÷ 32.1) = 0.1

   1 mol of Fe reacts with 1 mol of S

   Therefore, Fe is in excess (by 0.4 mol) and the mass of FeS obtained is determined by the no. of moles of S.

   1 mole of S $\rightarrow$ 1 mol FeS

   Therefore, 0.1 mol of S $\rightarrow$ 0.1 mol of FeS = 0.1 x (55.8 + 32.1) =

   8.79 g of FeS

3. $2H_2 + O_2 \rightarrow 2H_2O$

   2 mol of H_2 reacts with 1 mol of O_2

   Therefore, 0.2 mol of H_2 reacts with 0.1 mol of O_2.

   But. 0.1 mol of each reactant is used, therefore O_2 is in excess (by 0.05 mol) and the mass of H_2O obtained is determined by the no. of moles of H_2.

   2 mol of $H_2 \rightarrow$ 2 mol of H_2O

   Therefore, 0.1 mol of $H_2 \rightarrow$ 0.1 mol of H_2O = 0.1 x (2 + 16) = **1.8 g of H_2O**

4. $2Ca + O_2 \rightarrow 2CaO$
No. of moles of Ca = (30 ÷ 40.1) = 0.748;
No. of moles of O_2 = 0.25
2 mol of Ca reacts with 1 mol of O_2
Therefore, Ca is in excess (more than twice the number of moles of O_2)
and the mass of CaO obtained is determined by the amount of O_2.
1 mol of $O_2 \rightarrow$ 2 mol of CaO
Therefore, 0.25 mol of $O_2 \rightarrow$ 0.5 mol of CaO = 0.5 x (40.1 + 16) =
28.05 g of CaO

5. $(NH_4)_2SO_4 + 2NaOH \rightarrow 2NH_3 + Na_2SO_4 + 2H_2O$
No. of moles of $(NH_4)_2SO_4$ = 1.321 ÷ [(2x14) + (8x1) +32.1 + (4x16)] = 0.01
No. of moles of NaOH = 0.5 ÷ (23 + 16 + 1) = 0.0125
1 mol of $(NH_4)_2SO_4$ reacts with 2 mol of NaOH
But twice as many moles of NaOH are needed for complete reaction and
therefore, $(NH_4)_2SO_4$ is in excess and the mass of NH_3 is determined by the
amount of NaOH.
2 mol of NaOH $\rightarrow$ 2 mol of NH_3
Therefore, 0.0125 mol of NaOH $\rightarrow$ 0.0125 mol of NH_3
= 0.0125 x [14 + (3x1)] = **0.2125 g of NH$_3$**

6. *Take the molar volume of oxygen to be 23.2 litres mol^{-1}.*
$2Mg + O_2 \rightarrow 2MgO$
No. of moles of Mg = (2.43 ÷ 24.3) = 0.1;
No. of moles of O_2 = (10 ÷ 23.2) = 0.431
2 mol of Mg reacts with 1 mol of O_2
But twice as many moles of Mg are needed for complete reaction and
therefore, O_2 is in excess and the mass of MgO is determined by the mass
of Mg.
2 mol of Mg $\rightarrow$ 2 mol of MgO
Therefore, 0.1 mol of Mg $\rightarrow$ 0.1 mol of MgO = 0.1 x (24.3 + 16) =
4.03 g of MgO

Reminder: n = C x V or no. of moles = conc. x litres

7. $C_6H_8O_6 + I_2 \rightarrow C_6H_6O_6 + 2H^+ + 2I^-$
No. of moles of $C_6H_8O_6$ = (0.5 x 0.1) = 0.05;
No. of moles of I_2 = 10 ÷ (2 x 126.9) = 0.039
1 mol of $C_6H_8O_6$ reacts with 1 mol of I_2
Therefore, Vitamin C ($C_6H_8O_6$) is in excess and the **iodine solution would
have been decolourised**.

8. (a) $Zn + H_2SO_4 \rightarrow ZnSO_4 + H_2$
No. of moles of Zn = (6.54 ÷ 65.4) = 0.1;
No. of moles of H_2SO_4 = (2 x 0.025) = 0.05
1 mol of Zn reacts with 1 mol of H_2SO_4
Therefore, Zn is in excess and the amount of H_2 is determined by the amount of H_2SO_4.
1 mol of H_2SO_4 → 1 mol of H_2
Therefore, 0.05 mol of H_2SO_4 → 0.05 mol of H_2 = (0.05 x 23.2) =
16 litres of H_2

(b) $Mg + 2HCl \rightarrow MgCl_2 + H_2$
No. of moles of Mg = (2.43 ÷ 24.3) = 0.1;
No. of moles of HCl = (1 x 0.1) = 0.1
1 mol of Mg reacts with 2 mol of HCl
But twice as many moles of HCl are needed for complete reaction and therefore, Mg is in excess and the amount of H_2 is determined by the amount of HCl.
2 mol of HCl → 1 mol of H_2
Therefore, 0.1 mol of HCl → 0.05 mol of H_2 = (0.05 x 23.2) =
1.16 litres of H_2

(c) $Fe + 2HCl \rightarrow FeCl_2 + H_2$
No. of moles of Fe = (2.79 ÷ 55.8) = 0.05;
No. of moles of HCl = (0.5 x 0.08) = 0.04
1 mol of Fe reacts with 2 mol of HCl
But twice as many moles of HCl are needed for complete reaction and therefore, Fe is in excess and the amount of H_2 is determined by the amount of HCl.
2 mol of HCl → 1 mol of H_2
Therefore, 0.04 mol of HCl → 0.02 mol of H_2 = (0.02 x 23.2) =
0.464 litres of H_2

(d) $Mg + H_2SO_4 \rightarrow MgSO_4 + H_2$
No. of moles of Mg = (0.486 ÷ 24.3) = 0.02;
No. of moles of H_2SO_4 = (1 x 0.025) = 0.025
1 mol of Mg reacts with 1 mol of H_2SO_4
Therefore, H_2SO_4 is in excess and the amount of H_2 is determined by the mount of Mg.
1 mol of Mg → 1 mol of H_2
Therefore, 0.02 mol of Mg → 0.02 mol of H_2 = (0.02 x 23.2) =
0.464 litres of H_2

9. $Na_2SO_3 + 2HCl \rightarrow 2NaCl + H_2O + SO_2$

No. of moles of $Na_2SO_3 = 1.261 \div [(2 \times 23) + 32.1 + (3 \times 16)] = 0.01$;

No. of moles of $HCl = (2 \times 0.05) = 0.1$

1 mol of Na_2SO_3 reacts with 2 moles of HCl

Twice as many moles of HCl are needed for complete reaction, so HCl is in excess and the amount of SO_2 is determined by the amount of Na_2SO_3.

1 mol of $Na_2SO_3 \rightarrow$ 1 mol of SO_2

Therefore, 0.01 mol of $Na_2SO_3 \rightarrow$ 0.01 mol of $SO_2 = (0.01 \times 23.2)$

= **0.232 litres of SO_2**

Reminder: M = n x GFM or mass = no. of moles x GFM

---

10. $CaCO_3 + 2HNO_3 \rightarrow Ca(NO_3)_2 + H_2O + CO_2$

No. of moles of $CaCO_3 = 5 \div [40.1 + 12 + (3 \times 16)] = 5 \div 100.1 = 0.05$ mol;

No. of moles of $HNO_3 = 0.1 \times 0.1 = 0.01$ mol

1 mol of $CaCO_3$ reacts with 2mol of HNO_3

Therefore, 0.005 mol of $CaCO_3$ will react with 0.01 mol of HNO_3.

$CaCO_3$ is in excess by $(0.05 - 0.005) = 0.045$ mol $= 0.045 \times 100.1 = 4.5$ g

Calculations based on equations (iii)

Reminder: One mole of all gases have the same volume under the same conditions of temperature and pressure.

1. (a) H_2 (g) + Cl_2 (g) → 2HCl (g)
   2 mol of reactant gas → 2 mol of product gas
   Therefore, ratio of volume of product gas to volume of reactant gas is **1:1**

   (b) N_2 (g) + $3H_2$ (g) → $2NH_3$ (g)
   4 mol of reactant gas → 2 mol of product gas
   Therefore, ratio of volume of product gas to volume of reactant gas is **1:2**

   (c) 2C (s) + O_2 (g) → 2CO (g)
   1 mol of reactant gas → 2 mol of product gas
   Therefore, ratio of volume of product gas to volume of reactant gas is **2:1**

   (d) C_2H_4 (g) + $3O_2$ (g) → $2CO_2$ (g) + $2H_2O$ (l)
   4 mol of reactant gas → 2 mol of product gas
   Therefore, ratio of volume of product gas to volume of reactant gas is **1:2**

   (e) CuO (s) + CO (g) → Cu (s) + CO_2 (g)
   1 mol of reactant gas → 1 mol of product gas
   Therefore, ratio of volume of product gas to volume of reactant gas is **1:1**

2. N_2 (g) + $2O_2$ (g) → $2NO_2$ (g)
   1 mol of N_2 (g) reacts with 2 mol of O_2 (g) to produce 2 mol of NO_2 (g)
   Therefore, 100 cm^3 of N_2 (g) needs 200 cm^3 of O_2 (g) for complete reaction. However, only 150 cm^3 of oxygen is present.
   Therefore, 75 cm^3 of N_2 (g) reacts with 150 cm^3 of O_2 (g) to give
   150 cm^3 of NO_2 (g) (1:2:2 ratio)

3. $2P_2H_4$ (g) + $7 O_2$ (g) → P_4H_{10} (s) + $4 H_2O$ (l)
   2 mol of P_2H_4 reacts with 7 mol of O_2 (1 : 3.5 ratio)
   Therefore, 10 cm^3 of P_2H_4 reacts with 35 cm^3 of O_2
   Therefore, volume of unreacted oxygen = (50 – 35) = **15 cm^3**
   (2 : 7 ratio)

4. (a) CH_4 (g) + $2O_2$ (g) → CO_2 (g) + $2H_2O$ (l)
    1 mol of CH_4 (g) reacts with 2 mol of O_2 (g) to produce 1 mol of CO_2 (g)
    Therefore, 100 cm^3 of CH_4 needs **200 cm^3 of O_2** for complete reaction.
    100 cm^3 of CO_2 would be produced.   (1:2:1 ratio)

    (b) 2CO (g) + O_2 (g) → $2CO_2$ (g)
    2 mol of CO (g) reacts with 1 mol of O_2 (g) to produce 2 mol of CO_2 (g)
    Therefore, 2 litres of CO needs **1 litre of O_2** for complete reaction.
    2 litres of CO_2 would be produced.   (2:1:2 ratio)

    (c) C_2H_4 (g) + $3O_2$ (g) → $2CO_2$ (g) + $2H_2O$ (l)
    1 mol of C_2H_4 (g) reacts with 3 mol of O_2 (g) to produce 2 mol of CO_2 (g)
    Therefore, 250 cm^3 of C_2H_4 needs **750 cm^3 of O_2** for complete reaction.
    500 cm^3 of CO_2 would be produced.   (1:3:2 ratio)

    (d) C_4H_{10} (g) + $6.5O_2$ (g) → $4CO_2$ (g) + $5H_2O$ (l)
    1 mol of C_4H_{10} (g) reacts with 6.5 mol of O_2 (g) to produce 4 mol of CO_2 (g)
    Therefore, 150 cm^3 of C_4H_{10} needs (6.5 x 150) = **975 cm^3 of O_2** for
    complete reaction.
    (4 x 150) = **600 cm^3 of CO_2** would be produced.   (1 : 6.5 : 4 ratio)

5. C_3H_8 (g) + $5O_2$ (g) → $3CO_2$ (g) + $4H_2O$ (l)
    1 mol of C_3H_8 (g) reacts with 5 mol of O_2 (g) to produce 3 mol of CO_2 (g)
    Therefore, 10 cm^3 of C_3H_8 needs 50 cm^3 of O_2 for complete reaction.
    This means that (75 – 50) = **25 cm^3 of O_2** is unreacted.
    30 cm^3 of CO_2 would be produced.

6. (a) 2CO (g) + O_2 (g) → $2CO_2$ (g)

    (b) (i) carbon dioxide
    (ii) Gas ratio is 2:1:2. 80 cm^3 of CO reacts with 40 cm^3 of O_2 to produce
    80 cm^3 of CO_2. Therefore, the reduction in volume would be **80 cm^3** (the
    carbon dioxide gas).
    (iii) Only gas remaining would be unreacted O_2 with a volume of
    (150 – 40) = **110 cm^3**

7. The gas mixture contains 100 cm^3 of CH_4 and 100 cm^3 of H_2

CH_4 (g) + $2O_2$ (g) → CO_2 (g) + $2H_2O$ (l)

1 mol of CH_4 reacts with 2 mol of O_2

Therefore, 100 cm^3 of CH_4 needs **200 cm^3 of O_2**

$2H_2$ (g) + O_2 (g) → $2H_2O$ (l)

2 mol of H_2 reacts with 1 mol of O_2

Therefore, 100 cm^3 of H_2 needs **50 cm^3 of O_2**

The minimum volume of oxygen required is therefore **250 cm^3**

8. (a) Xe (g) + $3F_2$ (g) → XeF_6 (s)

(b) (i) 1 mol of Xe reacts with 3 mol of F_2

50 cm^3 of Xe needs 150 cm^3 of F_2 for complete reaction.

Therefore, **fluorine is in excess**.

ii) The only remaining gas will be the excess fluorine with a volume of

(400 – 150) = **250 cm^3**

9. $2H_2$ (g) + CuO (s) → Cu (s) + $2H_2O$ (l)

The reaction of the 60 cm^3 of H_2 would produce **no gas** (H_2O is a liquid at room temperature).

CO (g) + CuO (s) → Cu (s) + CO_2 (g)

1 mol of CO → 1 mol of CO_2 (g)

Therefore, 40 cm^3 of CO → **40 cm^3 of CO_2 (g)**

10. C_4H_{10} (g) + $6.5O_2$ (g) → $4CO_2$ (g) + $5H_2O$ (l)

1 mol of C_4H_{10} (g) reacts with 6.5 mol of O_2 (g) to produce 4 mol of CO_2 (g)

Therefore, 100 cm^3 of C_4H_{10} reacts with 650 cm^3 of O_2 to produce 400 cm^3 of CO_2.

This means that (900 – 650) i.e. **250 cm^3 of O_2** is left unreacted.

400 cm^3 of CO_2 would be produced.

i.e. volume and composition of the resulting gas mixture is **250 cm^3 of O_2** and **400 cm^3 of CO_2**.

11. If any hydrocarbon is completely burned all the carbon in the hydrocarbon becomes carbon dioxide. As 100 cm^3 of hydrocarbon produced 300 cm^3 of carbon dioxide, **x = 3**.

It is also known that 450 cm^3 of oxygen was used.

Therefore, C_3H_y + $4.5O_2$ (g) → $3CO_2$ (g) + ♦H_2O (l)

♦ must equal 3 to balance the O atoms and therefore **y = 6**.

12. (a) From the balanced equation the ratio of reactant gases is
    $1\ CO : 3\ H_2 : 2\ O_2$
    50 cm^3 of CO reacts with 150 cm^3 of H$_2$ and 100 cm^3 of O$_2$
    Therefore, **O$_2$ in excess** by (200 − 100) = **100 cm^3**
    (b) Ratio of product gases to $1CO : 3H_2 : 2O_2$ is $1CO_2 : 3H_2O$
    50 cm^3 of CO$_2$ (g) and **150 cm^3 of H$_2$O (g)** would be the product gases.
    (c) If at the end of the reaction the gases are cooled to room temperature the
    water produced as steam [H$_2$O (g)] will change to liquid water [H$_2$O (l)].
    The only remaining gases would be the 100 cm^3 of O$_2$ and 50 cm^3 of CO$_2$,
    giving a gas syringe reading of **150 cm^3**.

13. (a) 1 mol of a hydrocarbon containing 6 carbon atoms per molecule would
    produce 6 mol of carbon dioxide gas.
    Therefore, 20 cm^3 of the hydrocarbon would produce
    120 cm^3 of CO$_2$ (g)
    (b) If the complete reaction of 20 cm^3 of a hydrocarbon produces
    100 cm^3 of water vapour, i.e. 1:5 ratio, the hydrocarbon must contain 10
    hydrogen atoms per molecule. [$1C_xH_{10} \rightarrow 5H_2O$]
    Therefore, the molecular formula of the hydrocarbon is **C$_6$H$_{10}$**.

Dynamic equilibrium

1. (a) Many chemical reactions are reversible with the forward and backward reactions occurring at the same time. A chemical reaction is said to be at equilibrium when the rates of the forward and backward reactions are equal, and the concentration of the reactants and products constant.
      [Although **at equilibrium** the **rates are equal**, the **concentrations are constant** but unlikely to be equal.]
   (b) The word 'dynamic' is used because although at equilibrium the reactions may appear to have stopped because the concentrations are constant, they are actually still occurring, but at the same rate.

2. (a) If a chemical reaction is said to lie to the left at equilibrium, then at equilibrium the concentration of the reactants is greater than the concentration of the products.
   (b) If a chemical reaction is said to lie to the right at equilibrium, then at equilibrium the concentration of the products is greater than the concentration of the reactants.

3. (a)

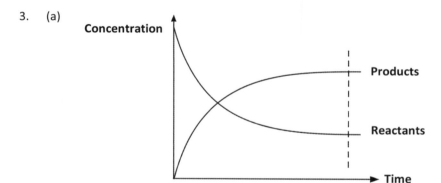

   (b) i) The equilibrium lies to the **right**.
      ii) At equilibrium (the point at which the concentrations of both reactants and products become constant) the concentration of the products is greater than the concentration of the reactants.

4.   The student is confusing either concentration with rate, or the words equal and constant.
      At equilibrium the rates of the forward and backward reactions are equal and the concentrations are constant.
      The concentrations could also be equal, but this is most unlikely.

5. (a) The equilibrium concentration of nitrogen dioxide will **increase**.
        [Increasing temperature – equilibrium will shift in the endothermic direction, and decreasing temperature – equilibrium will shift in the exothermic direction]
    (b) The equilibrium concentration of nitrogen dioxide will **decrease**.
        [Decreasing pressure – equilibrium will shift in the direction that increases the number of gaseous molecules, and
        increasing pressure – equilibrium will shift in the direction that decreases the number of gaseous molecules.]
    (c) The equilibrium concentration of nitrogen dioxide will **decrease**.
        [Addition of a reactant (or removal of a product) will favour the forward reaction – equilibrium will shift to the right, and
        addition of a product (or removal of a reactant) will favour the backward reaction – equilibrium will shift to the left.]

6. (a) The equilibrium will shift to the **right**.
    (b) The equilibrium will shift to the **right**.

7. (a) If more chlorine was added the equilibrium would shift to the right. Therefore, the mixture would contain less brown liquid and more yellow solid and would appear **lighter (less brown) in colour**.
    (b) If the temperature was increased the equilibrium would shift in the endothermic direction (right to left). Therefore, the mixture would contain more brown liquid and less yellow solid and would appear **darker (more brown) in colour**.
    (c) If the pressure was decreased the equilibrium would shift to the left to increase the number of gaseous molecules. Therefore, the mixture would contain more brown liquid and less yellow solid and would appear **darker (more brown) in colour**.

8. (a) Placing the equilibrium mixture in a freezing mixture would decrease the temperature. The equilibrium would shift in the exothermic direction (right to left). Therefore, the mixture would contain less brown gas and more yellow gas and would appear **lighter (less brown) in colour**.
    (b) If the equilibrium mixture is compressed, pressure is increased and the equilibrium would shift to the left (the side with fewer gaseous molecules). Therefore, the mixture would contain less brown gas and more yellow gas and would appear **lighter (less brown) in colour**.

9.   The forward reaction is exothermic. Decreasing the temperature from 400 °C to 80 °C will shift the equilibrium in the exothermic direction, i.e. left to right, increasing the yield of methane.
In addition, this decrease in temperature will change the water produced as steam [H_2O (g)] to liquid water [H_2O (l)]. This reduces the number of gaseous product molecules and also shifts the equilibrium from left to right, again increasing the yield of methane.

10. (a) The forward reaction is endothermic.
[Increasing temperature shifts the equilibrium in the endothermic direction. As synthesis gas is the product of the reaction and its yield is increased the forward reaction is endothermic.]
    (b) The equilibrium will shift to the left if pressure is increased, as this is the side with fewest gaseous molecules. If pressure is decreased the equilibrium will move to the right.

11. (a) A decrease in temperature can be thought of as removing energy from the equilibrium. The equilibrium will shift to oppose this change. Therefore, as the forward reaction is exothermic, more ethanol and energy will be produced to replace the energy that has been removed increasing the yield of ethanol.
    (b) If pressure is increased the equilibrium will shift to the right as this is the side with fewest gaseous molecules. As ethanol is on the right side its yield will increase.

12. (a) The equilibrium will shift to the **left**.
[Increasing temperature shifts the equilibrium in the endothermic direction.]
    (b) The equilibrium will shift to the **right**.
[Increasing pressure will shift the equilibrium to the side with fewest gaseous molecules.]
    (c) The equilibrium will shift to the **left**.
[Addition of alkali increases the concentration of OH⁻ ions. To oppose this change the equilibrium will shift to the left by reacting some of these additional ions.]
    (d) The equilibrium will shift to the **right**.
[Addition of acid puts H^+ ions into the mixture. These ions react with the OH⁻ ions. To replace the removed OH⁻ ions, the equilibrium will shift to the right.]

13. (a) An increase in pressure will
    i)   shift the position of equilibrium to the left in **Reactions 3 and 4**,
    ii)   have no effect on the equilibrium position in **Reaction 1**,
    iii) shift the position of equilibrium to the right in **Reaction 2**.
    [Increasing pressure will shift the equilibrium to the side with fewest gaseous molecules.]
    (b) Increasing temperature will shift the equilibrium in the endothermic direction (right to left).

14. (a) hydrogen chloride
    (b) The increase in concentratlon of hydrogen chloride shifts the equilibrium to the left and reduces the concentration of magnesium oxide that would form.

15. (a) The high temperature for both reactions is consistent with the need to reach equilibrium quickly.
        However, since both reactions are exothermic, the high temperature will shift the equilibria to the left, decreasing the yields and so is not consistent with the entropy changes involved
    (b) High pressure will cause the equilibrium in both processes to shift to the right, as the right side has fewer gaseous molecules. However, the cost of increasing the pressure, and hence the yield, may be justified in Process **A** but may be excessive in Process **B**.

16. (a) The use of a catalyst will
    (i) **increase** the rate of the forward reaction,
    (ii) **increase** the rate of the backward reaction,
    (iii) **increase** the rate of formation of product,
    (iv) **have no effect** on the composition of the equilibrium mixture.
    [A catalyst allows the equilibrium position to be reached more quickly, but as it increases the rates of both the forward and backward reactions it has no effect on the yield.]

(b) The number of gaseous molecules on each side of the equilibrium is not greatly different (3 to 2). As a result the relative increase in the rate of the forward reaction, by using higher pressures, cannot be justified by the increased cost of achieving these pressures.

(c) i) exothermic.
    ii) The yield decreases with increasing temperature for reactions that have an exothermic forward reaction.
    [An exothermic reaction gives out energy,
    i.e. reactants → products + 'energy'
    An increase in temperature can be thought of as adding energy. The equilibrium will shift to oppose this change, i.e. shift from right to left – decreasing yield.]

17. (a) The use of higher pressure will shift the equilibrium to the right, as the right side has fewer gaseous molecules. This will increase the yield of methanol.

(b) i) exothermic.
    ii) Since the yield is lower at 500 °C than at 300 °C, the equilibrium has shifted to the left to oppose this change to higher temperatures. The forward reaction must therefore be exothermic.

18. (a) Addition of hydrochloric acid puts more H^+ ions into the equilibrium mixture. The equilibrium will shift to oppose this change by reacting some of the added H^+ ions and will shift to the left producing more Br_2. The bromine solution will appear **darker (more brown) in colour**.

(b) The Ag^+ ions in the added silver nitrate solution react with the Br^- ions producing insoluble silver bromide. This equilibrium will shift to the right to replace the removed Br^- (aq) ions. The bromine solution will appear **lighter (less brown) in colour**.

19. (a) The bleaching efficiency would be **reduced**.
    [Adding nitric acid, puts more H^+ ions into the solution. This shifts the equilibrium to the left and reduces the concentration of ClO^- ions.]
    (b) The bleaching efficiency would be **reduced**.
    [Adding sodium chloride, puts more Cl^- ions into the solution. This shifts the equilibrium to the left and reduces the concentration of ClO^- ions.]
    (c) The bleaching efficiency would be **unaffected**.
    [Added sodium sulphate has no effect on the equilibrium.]
    (d) The bleaching efficiency would be **increased**.
    [Adding potassium hydroxide, puts OH^- ions into the solution. These ions react with the H^+ ions in the solution removing them. This shifts the equilibrium to the right and increases the concentration of ClO^- ions.]

20. (a) At equilibrium, equal numbers of iodine molecules move from the KI solution through the interface into the chloroform as move in the opposite direction.
    (b) When more chloroform is added, the iodine in chloroform solution is diluted and will become lighter. Iodine molecules from the KI solution will move through the interface to increase the concentration of iodine in chloroform solution.
    There will be a net transfer of iodine molecules from the KI solutlon. **The I_2 in chloroform layer will then become darker in colour and the I_2 in KI layer will then become lighter in colour** until equilibrium is re-established.

21. (a) **No effect** on the equilibrium mixture.
    [Nitric acid contains H^+ and NO_3^- ions. Neither of these ions are involved in the equilibrium or have any effect on it.]
    (b) The equilibrium will **shift to the left**.
    [Sulphuric acid contains H^+ and SO_4^{2-} ions. The added SO_4^{2-} ions react with the Ca^{2+} ions producing more $CaSO_4$ (s) shifting the equilibrium to the left.]
    (c) The equilibrium will **shift to the right**.
    [The added Ba^{2+} ions react with the SO_4^{2-} ions to produce insoluble barium sulphate. This removes SO_4^{2-} ions shifting the equilibrium to the right as more calcium sulphate dissolves to replace them.]

Percentage yield

1. (a) The actual yield in a chemical reaction is the quantity of desired product that is formed for a particular set of reaction conditions.
    (b) The theoretical yield is the quantity of desired product that is obtained assuming full conversion of the limiting reactant (the one not in excess), as calculated from the balanced equation.

2. $$Percentage\ yield = \frac{Actual\ yield}{Theoretical\ yield} \times 100$$

3. (a) 1 mol of C_3H_7OH → 1 mol of C_2H_5CHO
    $(3 \times 12) + (8 \times 1) + 16 = 60$ g of C_3H_7OH → $(3 \times 12) + (6 \times 1) + 16$
    $$= 58\ g\ of\ C_2H_5CHO$$
    Therefore, 3.9 g of C_3H_7OH → $3.9 \times (58 \div 60)$
    $$= 3.77\ g\ of\ C_2H_5CHO = Theoretical\ yield$$
    $$Percentage\ yield = \frac{Actual\ yield}{Theoretical\ yield} \times 100 = \frac{3.2}{3.77} \times 100 = \textbf{84.9\%}$$

    (b) 1 mol of C_3H_6 → 1 mol of $C_3H_6Br_2$
    $(3 \times 12) + (6 \times 1) = 42$ g of C_3H_6 → $(3 \times 12) + (6 \times 1) + (2 \times 79.9)$
    $$= 201.8\ g\ of\ C_3H_6Br_2$$
    Therefore, 5.2 g of C_3H_6 → $5.2 \times (201.8 \div 42)$
    $$= 25.0\ g\ of\ C_3H_6Br_2 = Theoretical\ yield$$
    $$Percentage\ yield = \frac{Actual\ yield}{Theoretical\ yield} \times 100 = \frac{20.4}{25.0} \times 100 = \textbf{81.6\%}$$

    (c) 1 mol of CH_3OH → 1 mol of $C_2H_5COOCH_3$
    $12 + (4 \times 1) + 16 = 32$ g of CH_3OH → $(4 \times 12) + (8 \times 1) + (2 \times 16)$
    $$= 88\ g\ of\ C_2H_5COOCH_3$$
    Therefore, 18.3 g of CH_3OH → $18.3 \times (88 \div 32)$
    $$= 50.3\ g\ of\ C_2H_5COOCH_3 = Theoretical\ yield$$
    $$Percentage\ yield = \frac{Actual\ yield}{Theoretical\ yield} \times 100 = \frac{40.4}{50.3} \times 100 = \textbf{80.3\%}$$

    (d) 3 mol of H_2 → 2 mol of NH_3
    $3 \times (2 \times 1) = 6$ g of H_2 → $2 \times [14 + (3 \times 1)] = 34$ g of NH_3
    Therefore, 2 kg of H_2 → $2 \times (34 \div 6)$
    $$= 11.33\ kg\ of\ NH_3 = Theoretical\ yield$$
    $$Percentage\ yield = \frac{Actual\ yield}{Theoretical\ yield} \times 100 = \frac{10}{11.33} \times 100 = \textbf{88.3\%}$$

3. (e) 1 mol of C_2H_4 → 1 mol of C_2H_5OH
(2x12) + (4x1) = 28 g of C_2H_4 → (2x12) + (6x1) + 16 = 46 g of C_2H_5OH
Therefore, 400 kg of C_2H_4 → 400 x (46 ÷ 28)
= 657 kg of C_2H_5OH = Theoretical yield
Percentage yield = $\dfrac{\text{Actual yield}}{\text{Theoretical yield}}$ x 100 = $\dfrac{580}{657}$ x 100 = **88.3%**

(f) 1 mol of SO_2 → 1 mol of SO_3
32.1 + (2x16) = 64.1 g of SO_2 → 32.1 + (3x16) = 80.1 g of SO_3
Therefore, 1 tonne of SO_2 → 1 x (80.1 ÷ 64.1) = 1.25 tonnes of SO_3 =
Theoretical yield
Percentage yield = $\dfrac{\text{Actual yield}}{\text{Theoretical yield}}$ x 100 = $\dfrac{0.83}{1.25}$ x 100 = **66.4%**

4. (a) 1 mol of ethanol C_2H_5OH → 1 mol of $CH_3COOC_2H_5$
(2x12) + (6x1) + 16 = 46 g of C_2H_5OH → (4x12) + (8x1) + (2x16)
= 88 g of $CH_3COOC_2H_5$
Therefore, 4.6 g of C_2H_5OH → 88 x (4.6 ÷ 46) = 8.8 g of $CH_3COOC_2H_5$
However, if percentage yield is 81%, the mass of ethylethanoate
obtained = (81 ÷ 100) x 8.8 g = **7.13 g**

(b) 1 mol of CH_3CHO → 1 mol of CH_3COOH
(2x12) + (4x1) + 16 = 44 g of CH_3CHO → (2x12) + (4x1) + (2x16)
= 60 g of CH_3COOH
Therefore, 2.7 g of CH_3CHO → 60 x (2.7 ÷ 44) = 3.68 g of CH_3COOH
However, if percentage yield is 63%, the mass of ethanoic acid obtained
= (63 ÷ 100) x 3.68 g = **2.32 g**

(c) 1 mol of C_2H_4 → 1 mol of C_2H_5OH
(2x12) + (4x1) = 28 g of C_2H_4 → (2x12) + (6x1) + 16 = 46 g of C_2H_5OH
Therefore, 1000 kg of C_2H_4 → 46 x (1000 ÷ 28) = 1643 kg of C_2H_5OH
However, if percentage yield is 80%, the mass of ethanol obtained
= (80 ÷ 100) x 1643 kg = **1314 kg**

(d) 1 mol of CH_3COOCH_3 → 1 mol of HCOOH
(3x12) + (6x1) + (2x16) = 74 g of CH_3COOCH_3 → (2x1) + 12 + (2x16)
= 46 g of HCOOH
Therefore, 2.1 g of CH_3COOCH_3 → 46 x (2.1 ÷ 74) = 1.305 g of HCOOH
However, if percentage yield is 73%, the mass of methanoic acid
obtained = (73 ÷ 100) x 1.305 g = **0.95 g**

4. (e) 1 mol of SO_2 → 1 mol of SO_3
        $32.1 + (2 \times 16) = 64.1$ g of SO_2 → $32.1 + (3 \times 16) = 80.1$ g of SO_3
        Therefore, 250 kg of SO_2 → $80.1 \times (250 \div 64.1) = 312$ kg of SO_3
        However, if percentage yield is 71%, the mass of sulphur dioxide obtained
        = $(71 \div 100) \times 312$ kg = **222 kg**

    (f) 4 mol of NH_3 → 4 mol of NO_2
        Therefore, 1 mol of NH_3 → 1 mol of NO_2
        $14 + (3 \times 1) = 17$ g of NH_3 → $14 + (2 \times 16) = 46$ g of NO_2
        Therefore, 10 tonnes of NH_3 → $46 \times (10 \div 17) = 27.1$ tonnes of NO_2
        However, if percentage yield is 67%, the mass of nitrogen dioxide
        obtained = $(67 \div 100) \times 27.1$ tonnes = **18.2 tonnes**

Atom economy

1. (a) The atom economy of a chemical reaction is the proportion of the total mass that is successfully converted into the desired product.

   (b) $$\text{Atom economy} = \frac{\text{Mass of desired product(s)}}{\text{Total mass of reactants}} \times 100$$

2. Reactions with a high atom economy can be considered 'greener' because there is less waste product.

3. (a)

C_2H_4	+	H_2O	→	C_2H_5OH
1 mol		1 mol		1 mol
$(2 \times 12) + (4 \times 1)$		$(2 \times 1) + 16$		$(2 \times 12) + 6 + 16$
28 g		18 g		46 g

$$\text{Atom economy} = \frac{\text{Mass of desired product(s)}}{\text{Total mass of reactants}} \times 100$$

$$= \frac{46}{46} \times 100 = \mathbf{100\%}$$

(b)

Fe_2O_3	+	3CO	→	2Fe	+	CO_2
1 mol		3 mol		2 mol		Not desired product
$(2 \times 55.8) + (3 \times 16)$		$3 \times (12 + 16)$		2×55.8		
159.6 g		84 g		111.6 g		

$$\text{Atom economy} = \frac{\text{Mass of desired product(s)}}{\text{Total mass of reactants}} \times 100$$

$$= \frac{111.6}{243.6} \times 100 = \mathbf{45.8\%}$$

(c)

$CaCO_3$	→	CaO	+	CO_2
1 mol		1 mol		Not desired product
$40.1 + 12 + (3 \times 16)$		$40.1 + 16$		
100.1 g		56.1 g		

$$\text{Atom economy} = \frac{\text{Mass of desired product(s)}}{\text{Total mass of reactants}} \times 100$$

$$= \frac{56.1}{100.1} \times 100 = \mathbf{56.0}$$

3. (d) $C_6H_{12}O_6$ $\rightarrow$ 2 C_2H_5OH + CO_2

1 mol   2 mol   Not desired

$(6\times12) + (12) + (6\times16)$ $2 \times [(2\times12) + 6 + 16]$ product

180 g   92 g

Atom economy $= \dfrac{\text{Mass of desired product(s)}}{\text{Total mass of reactants}} \times 100 \quad = \dfrac{92}{180} \times 100$

$= \mathbf{51.1\%}$

(e) $2NH_3$ + NaOCl $\rightarrow$ N_2H_4 + NaCl + H_2O

1 mol   1 mol   1 mol   Not desired products

$2 \times [14 + (3\times1)]$ $23 + 16 + 35.5$ $(2\times14) + (4\times1)$

34 g   74.5 g   32 g

Atom economy $= \dfrac{\text{Mass of desired product(s)}}{\text{Total mass of reactants}} \times 100 \quad = \dfrac{32}{108.5} \times 100$

$= \mathbf{29.5\%}$

4. (a) N_2 + $3H_2$ $\rightarrow$ $2NH_3$

1 mol   3 mol   2 mol

(2×14)   3 × (2×1) $2 \times [14 + (3\times1)]$

28 g   6 g   34 g

Atom economy $= \dfrac{\text{Mass of desired product(s)}}{\text{Total mass of reactants}} \times 100 \quad = \dfrac{34}{34} \times 100$

$= \mathbf{100\%}$

CaO + $2NH_4Cl$ $\rightarrow$ $CaCl_2$ + H_2O + $2NH_3$

1 mol   2 mol   Not desired products   2 mol

40.1 + 16 $2 \times [14 + (4\times1) + 35.5]$ $2 \times [14+(3\times1)]$

56.1 g   107 g   34 g

Atom economy $= \dfrac{\text{Mass of desired product(s)}}{\text{Total mass of reactants}} \times 100 \quad = \dfrac{34}{163.1} \times 100$

$= \mathbf{20.8\%}$

(b) i) Producing ammonia by the Haber Process can be considered to be greener.

ii) The Haber Process is greener as it is much more efficient in terms of atom economy.

Enthalpy of combustion

1. The enthalpy of combustion of a substance is the heat given out when one mole of the substance burns completely in oxygen.

2. (a) CH_3OH (l) + $1.5O_2$ (g) → CO_2 (g) + $2H_2O$ (l)
    [Equation must be balanced for **one mole** of the substance being burned.]
    (b) C_2H_5OH (l) + $3O_2$ (g) → $2CO_2$ (g) + $3H_2O$ (l)

3. Energy being lost to the apparatus and surrounding air and incomplete combustion of the alcohol are two reasons for the enthalpy of combustion value calculated in the laboratory being different (usually considerably lower) than the Data Booklet value.

4. Although both substances have the same molecular formula, different bonds are broken on combustion and this leads to different values for their enthalpies of combustion.
    [Dimethyl ether has 6 C–H bonds and 2 C–O bonds;
    ethanol has 5 C–H bonds, 1 C–O bond and 1 O–H bond.]

5. (a) Each substance differs from the previous one by the addition of one –CH$_2$– group. This constant difference in structure leads to a regular increase in the values of enthalpy of combustion.
    (b) Any answer between -2670 and -2700 kJ mol^{-1}.
    [The differences in enthalpy of combustions of the successive substances are -641 and -654. Assuming that this pattern continues to butan-1-ol, a difference of about -667 could be estimated.
    This would give an enthalpy of combustion of -2688 kJ mol^{-1}.]

6. (a) 1 mole of ethane (C_2H_6) has a mass of (2x12) + (6x1) = 30 g
    Therefore, energy given out on combustion of 1 mole = 30 x 50 kJ
    = 1500 kJ.
    Therefore, enthalpy of combustion of ethane is **–1500 kJ mol^{-1}**.
    [Negative sign as energy is given out, i.e. exothermic reaction.]

    (b) 1 mole of butane (C_4H_{10}) has a mass of (4x12) + (10x1) = 58 g
    10 g of butane gave out 469 kJ.
    Therefore, enthalpy given out on combustion of 1 mole =
    469 x (58 ÷10) kJ = 2720 kJ.
    Therefore, enthalpy of combustion of ethane is **–2720 kJ mol^{-1}**.

Reminder:

Heat released = E_h = cmΔT

where c = specific heat capacity of water = 4.18 kJ kg^{-1} $^\circ$C^{-1}

m = mass of <u>water</u> absorbing heat in kilograms

(1 cm^3 of water has a mass of 1 g = 0.001 kg)

ΔT = temperature change

7. (a) 1 mole of methanol (CH_3OH) has a mass of 12 + (4x1) + 16 = 32 g
    E_h by burning 1.1 g of methanol = cmΔT = 4.18 x 0.1 x 57 = 23.83 kJ
    Therefore, enthalpy of combustion = (32 ÷ 1.1) x 23.83 = **−693 kJ mol^{-1}**

    (b) 1 mole of ethanol (C_2H_5OH) has a mass of (2x12) + (6x1) + 16 = 46 g
    E_h by burning 5.9 g of ethanol = cmΔT = 4.18 x 1 x 39.1 = 163.4 kJ
    Therefore, enthalpy of combustion = (46 ÷ 5.9) x 163.4 = **−1274 kJ mol^{-1}**

8.   1 mole of sulphur (S) has a mass of 32.1 g
    E_h by burning 1 g of sulphur = cmΔT = 4.18 x 0.110 x 20 = 9.196 kJ
    Therefore, enthalpy of combustion = 32.1 x 9.196 = **−295 kJ mol^{-1}**

9. (a) Enthalpy of combustion of ethene is −1411 kJ mol^{-1} (Data Booklet)
    1 mole of ethene (C_2H_4) has a mass of (2x12) + (4x1) = 28 g
    Therefore, combustion of 28 g of ethene would give out 1411 kJ
    Therefore, combustion of 1 g of ethene would give out
    (1 ÷ 28) x 1411 kJ = **50.4 kJ**

    (b) Enthalpy of combustion of hydrogen is −286 kJ mol^{-1} (Data Booklet)
    1 mole of hydrogen (H_2) has a mass of (2x1) = 2 g
    Therefore, combustion of 2 g of hydrogen would give out 286 kJ
    Therefore, combustion of 8 g of hydrogen would give out
    (8 ÷ 2) x 286 kJ = **1144 kJ**

10. (a) Enthalpy of combustion of methane is −891 kJ mol^{-1} (Data Booklet)
    1 mole of methane (CH_4) has a mass of 12 + (4x1) = 16 g
    Therefore, combustion of 16 g of methane would give out 891 kJ
    Therefore, mass of methane that would give out 21.3 kJ
    $= (21.3 ÷ 891)$ x 16 = **0.38 g**

    (b) Enthalpy of combustion of propane is −2219 kJ mol^{-1} (Data Booklet)
    1 mole of propane (C_3H_8) has a mass of (3x12) + (8x1) = 44 g
    Therefore, combustion of 44 g of propane would give out 2219 kJ
    Therefore, mass of propane that would give out 5000 kJ
    $= (5000 ÷ 2219)$ x 44 = **99.1 g**

11. (a) Enthalpy of combustion of methanol is -726 kJ mol^{-1} (Data Booklet)
1 mole of methanol (CH_3OH) has a mass of 12 + (4x1) + 16 = 32 g
Therefore, combustion of 32 g of methanol would give out 726 kJ
E_h by burning the methanol = cmΔT = 4.18 x 2 x 63 = 526.7 kJ
Therefore, mass of methanol burned = (526.7 ÷ 726) x 32 = **23.2 g**

(b) Enthalpy of combustion of ethanol is -1367 kJ mol^{-1} (Data Booklet)
1 mole of ethanol (C_2H_5OH) has a mass of (2x12) + (6x1) + 16 = 46 g
Therefore, combustion of 46 g of ethanol would give out 1367 kJ
E_h by burning the ethanol = cmΔT = 4.18 x 0.5 x 34.5 = 72.1 kJ
Therefore, mass of ethanol burned = (72.1 ÷ 1367) x 46 = **2.43 g**

Hess's Law

1. (a) $a = b - c$
   (b) Hess's Law states that the enthalpy change in converting reactants into products is the same regardless of the route by which the reaction takes place.

   > The worked examples that follow show only one approach to tackling Hess's Law calculations. Equally good alternative methods can also be used.

2. Required equation

NaOH (s)	→ NaOH (aq)	ΔH = ?

   Given equations

1.	NaOH (s)	+	HCl (aq)	→ NaCl (aq)	+	H_2O (l)	−105
2.	NaOH (aq)	+	HCl (aq)	→ NaCl (aq)	+	H_2O (l)	−65.8

   Build up of required equation using given equations

1.	NaOH (s)	+	~~HCl (aq)~~	→ ~~NaCl (aq)~~	+	~~H_2O (l)~~	−105
Rev 2.	~~NaCl (aq)~~	+	~~H_2O (l)~~	→ NaOH (aq)	+	~~HCl (aq)~~	+65.8

   [Rev = reverse of given equation;
   when an equation is reversed the sign of the ΔH changes.]

   Cancelling and adding gives the required equation.
   Therefore, ΔH = −105 + 65.8 = **−39.2 kJ mol^{-1}**

3. Required equation

RbCl (s)	→ Rb$^+$ (g)	+ Cl$^-$ (g)	ΔH = ?

   Given equations

1.	RbCl (s)	→ Rb$^+$ (aq)	+ Cl$^-$ (aq)	+17
2.	Rb$^+$ (g)	→ Rb$^+$ (aq)		−301
3.	Cl$^-$ (g)	→ Cl$^-$ (aq)		−364

   Build up of required equation using given equations

1.	RbCl (s)	→ ~~Rb$^+$ (aq)~~	+	~~Cl$^-$ (aq)~~	+17
Rev 2.	~~Rb$^+$ (aq)~~	→ Rb$^+$ (g)			+301
Rev 3.	~~Cl$^-$ (aq)~~	→ Cl$^-$ (g)			+364

   Cancelling and adding gives the required equation.
   Therefore, ΔH = +17 + 301 + 364 = **+682 kJ mol^{-1}**

4.   Required equation

$$CO\ (g) \quad + \quad \tfrac{1}{2} O_2\ (g) \quad \rightarrow \quad CO_2\ (g) \qquad\qquad \mathbf{\Delta H = ?}$$

[The required equation must be balanced for one mole of CO as it represents the enthalpy of combustion of carbon monoxide.]

Given equations

1.	$2C\ (g)$	$+$	$O_2\ (g)$	$\rightarrow \quad 2CO\ (g)$	-216
2.	$C\ (g)$	$+$	$O_2\ (g)$	$\rightarrow \quad CO_2\ (g)$	-394

Build up of required equation using given equations

½ of Rev 1. $CO\ (g) \qquad\qquad\qquad \rightarrow \quad \cancel{C\ (g)} \quad + \quad \cancel{\tfrac{1}{2} O_2\ (g)} \qquad +108$

2. $C\ (g) \quad + \quad \cancel{O_2\ (g)} \quad \rightarrow \quad CO_2\ (g) \qquad\qquad -394$

$\tfrac{1}{2} O_2$

[ΔH of first build up equation is both halved and has sign changed and ½ O_2 (g) on 'product' side cancels half of the O_2 (g) on 'reactant' side.]

Cancelling and adding gives the required equation.
Therefore, ΔH = + 108 + (−394) = **−286 kJ mol^{-1}**

5.   Required equation

$$3C\ (g) \quad + \quad 4H_2\ (g) \quad \rightarrow \quad C_3H_8\ (g) \qquad\qquad \mathbf{\Delta H = ?}$$

Given equations

1.	$C\ (s)$		$\rightarrow \quad C\ (g)$	$+715$
2.	$3C\ (s)$	$+ \quad 4H_2\ (g)$	$\rightarrow \quad C_3H_8\ (g)$	-104

Build up of required equation using given equations

3 x Rev 1. $3C\ (g) \qquad\qquad\qquad \rightarrow \quad \cancel{3C\ (s)} \qquad\qquad -2145$

2. $\cancel{3C\ (s)} \quad + \quad 4H_2\ (g) \quad \rightarrow \quad C_3H_8\ (g) \qquad -104$

Cancelling and adding gives the required equation.
Therefore, ΔH = −2145 + (−104) = **−2249 kJ mol^{-1}**

6. Required equation

      C_2H_4 (g)   + H_2 (g)   → C_2H_6 (g) $ΔH$ = ?

Given equations

1. H_2 (g)   +   ½ O_2 (g)   → H_2O (l)   −286
2. C_2H_4 (g)   + $3O_2$ (g)   → $2CO_2$ (g)   + $2H_2O$ (l)   −1411
3. C_2H_6 (g)   +   3½ O_2 (g) → $2CO_2$ (g)   + $3H_2O$ (l)   −1561

Build up of required equation using given equations

2. C_2H_4 (g)   +   ~~$3O_2$ (g)~~   →   ~~$2CO_2$ (g)~~   +   ~~$2H_2O$ (l)~~   −1411
1. H_2 (g)   +   ~~½ O_2 (g)~~   →   ~~H_2O (l)~~   −286
Rev 3.   ~~$2CO_2$ (g)~~   +   ~~$3H_2O$ (l)~~   → C_2H_6 (g)   +   ~~3½ O_2 (g)~~   +1561

Cancelling and adding gives the required equation.
Therefore, $ΔH$ = −1411 + (−286) + 1561 = **−136 kJ mol^{-1}**

7. Required equation

       3C (s)   + H_2 (g)   + Cl_2 (g)   → CH_2Cl_2 (g)   **$ΔH$ = ?**

Given equations

1. CH_2Cl_2 (g)   + O_2 (g)   → CO_2 (g)   +   2HCl (g)   −446
2.   C (s)   + O_2 (g)   → CO_2 (g)   −394
3. H_2 (g)   + Cl_2 (g)   →   2HCl (g)   −104

Build up of required equation using given equations

3 x 2.   3C (s)   +   ~~O_2 (g)~~   →   ~~CO_2 (g)~~   −1182
3. H_2 (g)   + Cl_2 (g)   →   ~~2HCl (g)~~   −104
Rev 1.   ~~CO_2 (g)~~   +   ~~2HCl (g)~~   → CH_2Cl_2 (g)   +   ~~O_2 (g)~~   +446

Cancelling and adding gives the required equation.
Therefore, $ΔH$ = −1182 + (−104) + 446 = **−840 kJ mol^{-1}**

8.   **Required equation**

          $2C\ (s)$ + $3H_2\ (g)$ + $\tfrac{1}{2}O_2\ (g)$ → $C_2H_5OH\ (l)$ **ΔH = ?**

       Given equations

1.	$C\ (s)$ + $O_2\ (g)$	→	$CO_2\ (g)$		−394
2.	$H_2\ (g)$ + $\tfrac{1}{2}O_2\ (g)$	→	$H_2O\ (l)$		−286
3.	$C_2H_5OH\ (l)$ + $3O_2\ (g)$	→	$2CO_2\ (g)$ + $3H_2O\ (l)$		−1367

       Build up of required equation using given equations

2 x 1. $2C\ (s)$ + $\cancel{2O_2\ (g)}$ → $\cancel{2CO_2\ (g)}$ −788

3 x 2. $3H_2\ (g)$ + $\cancel{1\tfrac{1}{2}O_2\ (g)}$ → $\cancel{3H_2O\ (l)}$ −858

Rev 3. $\cancel{2CO_2\ (g)}$ + $\cancel{3H_2O\ (l)}$ → $C_2H_5OH\ (l)$ + $\cancel{3O_2\ (g)}$ +1367

       Cancelling and adding gives the required equation.

       Therefore, ΔH = −788 + (−858) + 1367 = **−279 kJ mol^{-1}**

9.   **Required equation**

          $3C\ (s)$ + $4H_2\ (g)$ + $\tfrac{1}{2}O_2\ (g)$ → $C_3H_7OH\ (l)$ **ΔH = ?**

       Given equations

1.	$C\ (s)$ + $O_2\ (g)$	→	$CO_2\ (g)$		−394
2.	$H_2\ (g)$ + $\tfrac{1}{2}O_2\ (g)$	→	$H_2O\ (l)$		−286
3.	$C_3H_7OH\ (l)$ + $4\tfrac{1}{2}O_2\ (g)$	→	$3CO_2\ (g)$ + $4H_2O\ (l)$		−2021

       Build up of required equation using given equations

3 x 1. $3C\ (s)$ + $\cancel{3O_2\ (g)}$ → $\cancel{3CO_2\ (g)}$ −1182

4 x 2. $4H_2\ (g)$ + $\cancel{2O_2\ (g)}$ → $\cancel{4H_2O\ (l)}$ −1144

                  $\tfrac{1}{2}O_2$

Rev 3. $\cancel{3CO_2\ (g)}$ + $\cancel{4H_2O\ (l)}$ → $C_3H_7OH\ (l)$ + $\cancel{4\tfrac{1}{2}O_2\ (g)}$ +2021

       Cancelling and adding gives the required equation.

       Therefore, ΔH = −1182 + (−1144) + 2021 = **−305 kJ mol^{-1}**

10.   Required equation

$$4C (s) \quad + \quad 5H_2 (g) \quad \rightarrow \quad C_4H_{10} (g) \qquad \qquad \Delta H = ?$$

Given equations

1.	C_4H_{10} (g	+	$6\frac{1}{2} O_2$ (g)	$\rightarrow$ $4CO_2$ (g)	+ $5H_2O$ (l)	−2878
2.	C (s)	+	O_2 (g)	$\rightarrow$ CO_2 (g)		−394
3.	H_2 (g)	+	$\frac{1}{2} O_2$ (g)	$\rightarrow$ H_2O (l)		−286

Build up of required equation using given equations

4 x 2.	4C (s)	+	4O_2 (g)	$\rightarrow$ 4CO_2 (g)		−1576
5 x 3.	$5H_2$ (g)	+	2½ O_2 (g)	$\rightarrow$ 5H_2O (l)		−1430
Rev 1.	4CO_2 (g)	+	5H_2O (l)	$\rightarrow$ C_4H_{10} (g)	+ 6½ O_2 (g)	+2878

Cancelling and adding gives the required equation.
Therefore, ΔH = −1576 + (−1430) + 2878 = **−128 kJ mol^{-1}**

11.   Required equation

$$6C (s) \quad + \quad 6H_2 (g) \quad \rightarrow \quad C_6H_{12} (l) \qquad \qquad \Delta H = ?$$

The balanced equation should have $6H_2$ not $3H_2$.

Given equations

1.	C (s)	+	O_2 (g)	$\rightarrow$ CO_2 (g)		−394
2.	H_2 (g)	+	$\frac{1}{2} O_2$ (g)	$\rightarrow$ H_2O (l)		−286
3.	C_6H_{12} (l)	+	$9O_2$ (g)	$\rightarrow$ $6CO_2$ (g)	+ $6H_2O$ (l)	−3920

Build up of required equation using given equations

6 x 1.	6C (s)	+	6O_2 (g)	$\rightarrow$ $6CO_2$ (g)		−2364
6 x 2.	$6H_2$ (g)	+	3O_2 (g)	$\rightarrow$ 6H_2O (l)		−1716
Rev 3.	$6CO_2$ (g)	+	6H_2O (l)	$\rightarrow$ C_6H_{12} (l)	+ 9O_2 (g)	+3920

Cancelling and adding gives the required equation.
Therefore, ΔH = −2364 + (−1716) + 3920 = **−160 kJ mol^{-1}**

12.   **Required equation**

$$2C \text{ (s)} \quad + \quad 3H_2 \text{ (g)} \quad \rightarrow \quad C_2H_6 \text{ (g)} \qquad \qquad \Delta H = ?$$

Given equations

1.	$C \text{ (s)}$	$+ \quad O_2 \text{ (g)}$	$\rightarrow \quad CO_2 \text{ (g)}$	-394
2.	$H_2 \text{ (g)}$	$+ \quad \frac{1}{2} O_2 \text{ (g)}$	$\rightarrow \quad H_2O \text{ (l)}$	-286
3.	$C_2H_6 \text{ (g)}$	$+ \quad 3\frac{1}{2} O_2 \text{ (g)}$	$\rightarrow \quad 2CO_2 \text{ (g)} \quad + \quad 3H_2O \text{ (l)}$	-1561

Build up of required equation using given equations

2 x 1.	$2C \text{ (s)}$	$+ \quad \cancel{2O_2 \text{ (g)}}$	$\rightarrow \quad \cancel{2CO_2 \text{ (g)}}$	-788
3 x 2.	$3H_2 \text{ (g)}$	$+ \quad \cancel{1\frac{1}{2} O_2 \text{ (g)}}$	$\rightarrow \quad \cancel{3H_2O \text{ (l)}}$	-858
Rev 3.	$\cancel{2CO_2 \text{ (g)}}$	$+ \quad \cancel{3H_2O \text{ (l)}}$	$\rightarrow \quad C_2H_6 \text{ (g)} \quad + \quad \cancel{3\frac{1}{2} O_2 \text{ (g)}}$	$+1561$

Cancelling and adding gives the required equation.

Therefore, $\Delta H = -788 + (-858) + 1561 =$ **-85 kJ mol^{-1}**

13.   **Required equation**

$$C \text{ (s)} \quad + \quad 3H_2 \text{ (g)} \quad + \quad N_2 \text{ (g)} \quad \rightarrow \quad CH_3NHNH_2 \text{ (l)} \qquad \Delta H = ?$$

Given equations

1.	$CH_3NHNH_2 \text{ (l)} + 2\frac{1}{2} O_2 \text{ (g)} \rightarrow CO_2 \text{ (g)} + 3H_2O \text{ (l)} + N_2 \text{ (g)}$		-1305
2.	$C \text{ (s)}$	$+ \quad O_2 \text{ (g)} \quad \rightarrow \quad CO_2 \text{ (g)}$	-394
3.	$H_2 \text{ (g)}$	$+ \quad \frac{1}{2} O_2 \text{ (g)} \quad \rightarrow \quad H_2O \text{ (l)}$	-286

Build up of required equation using given equations

2.	$C \text{ (s)}$	$+ \quad \cancel{O_2 \text{ (g)}} \quad \rightarrow \quad \cancel{CO_2 \text{ (g)}}$	-394
3 x 3.	$3H_2 \text{ (g)}$	$+ \quad \cancel{1\frac{1}{2} O_2 \text{ (g)}} \quad \rightarrow \quad \cancel{3H_2O \text{ (l)}}$	-858
Rev 1.	$\cancel{CO_2 \text{ (g)}} + \cancel{3H_2O \text{ (l)}} + N_2 \text{ (g)} \rightarrow CH_3NHNH_2 \text{ (l)} + \cancel{2\frac{1}{2} O_2 \text{ (g)}}$		$+1305$

Cancelling and adding gives the required equation.

Therefore, $\Delta H = -788 + (-858) + 1561 =$ **$+53$ kJ mol^{-1}**

14.   Required equation
B_2H_6 (g)   + $3O_2$ (g)   → B_2O_3 (s)   + $3H_2O$ (l)   **ΔH = ?**

Given equations
1.   2B (s)   + $3H_2$ (g)   → B_2H_6 (g)   +32
2. H_2 (g)   + $\frac{1}{2} O_2$ (g)   → H_2O (l)   −286
3.   2B (s)   + $1\frac{1}{2} O_2$ (g   → B_2O_3 (s)   −1225

Build up of required equation using given equations
Rev 1. B_2H_6 (g)   →   ~~2B (s)~~   +   ~~$3H_2$ (g)~~   −32
3.   ~~2B (s)~~   + $1\frac{1}{2} O_2$ (g)   → B_2O_3 (s)   −1225
3 x 2.   ~~$3H_2$ (g)~~   + $1\frac{1}{2} O_2$ (g)   → $3H_2O$ (l)   −858

Cancelling and adding gives the required equation.
Therefore, ΔH = −32 + (−1225) + (−858) = **−2115 kJ mol^{-1}**

15.   Required equation
2C (s)   + $2H_2$ (g)   + O_2 (g)   → CH_3COOH (l)   **ΔH = ?**

Given equations
The balanced equation for 1 should have two H_2O (l) not one H_2O (l).
1. CH_3COOH (l)   + $2O_2$ (g)   → $2CO_2$ (g)   + $2H_2O$ (l)   -876
2.   C (s)   + O_2 (g)   → CO_2 (g)   −394
3. H_2 (g)   + $\frac{1}{2} O_2$ (g)   → H_2O (l)   −286

Build up of required equation using given equations
2 x 2.   2C (s)   +   ~~$2O_2$ (g)~~   →   ~~$2CO_2$ (g)~~   −788
2 x 3. $2H_2$ (g)   + O_2 (g)   →   ~~$2H_2O$ (l)~~   −572
Rev 1.   ~~$2CO_2$ (g)~~   +   ~~$2H_2O$ (l)~~   → CH_3COOH (l)   +   ~~$2O_2$ (g)~~   +876

Cancelling and adding gives the required equation.
Therefore, ΔH = −788 + (−572) + 876 = **−484 kJ mol^{-1}**

Bond enthalpy

1. (a) Bond breaking is an **endothermic** reaction.
    (b) Bond making is an **exothermic** reaction.

2. (a) Bond enthalpy is the energy required to break one mole of bonds.
    (b) Mean bond enthalpy is the average energy required to break one mole of bonds.
         [An average value is necessary because the strength of the covalent bond between two different atoms varies slightly from one compound to another.]
    (c) The C–H bond is listed as a mean bond enthalpy because the strength of the bond varies slightly from one compound to another. However, the Cl–Cl bond only exists in Cl_2 and therefore a mean value is not necessary.

3. (a)
Bonds broken		New bonds formed	
1 mol C=C	= 612	1 mol C–C	= 348
1 mol Cl–Cl	= 243	2 mol C–Cl = 2 x 338	= 676
Total energy in =	+855	Total energy out =	−1024

ΔH = +855−1024 = **−169 kJ mol^{-1}**

    (b)
Bonds broken		New bonds formed	
1 mol C–H	= 412	1 mol C–Br	= 276
1 mol Br–Br	= 194	1 mol H–Br	= 366
Total energy in =	+606	Total energy out =	−642

ΔH = +606−642 = **−36 kJ mol^{-1}**

    (c)
Bonds broken		New bonds formed	
2 mol C=C = 2 x 612	= 1224	2 mol C–C = 2 x 348	= 696
2 mol H–H = 2 x 436	= 872	4 mol C–H = 4 x 412	= 1648
Total energy in =	+2096	Total energy out =	−2344

ΔH = +2096−2344 = **−248 kJ mol^{-1}**

3. (d)

Bonds broken		New bonds formed	
1 mol C≡C	= 838	1 mol C−C	= 348
2 mol H−H = 2 x 436	= 872	4 mol C−H = 4 x 412	= 1648
Total energy in =	+1710	Total energy out =	−1996

ΔH = +1710−1996 = **−286 kJ mol⁻¹**

(e)

Bonds broken		New bonds formed	
1 mol H−H	= 436	2 mol H−F = 2 x 570	= 1140
1 mol F−F	= 159		
Total energy in =	+595	Total energy out =	−1140

ΔH = +595−1140 = **−545 kJ mol⁻¹**

(f)

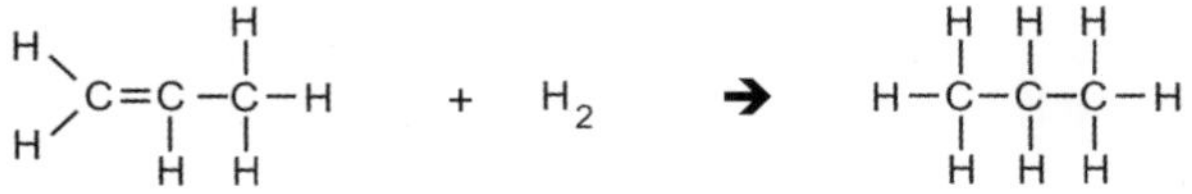

Bonds broken		New bonds formed	
1 mol C=C	= 612	1 mol C−C	= 348
1 mol H−H	= 243	2 mol C−H = 2 x 412	= 824
Total energy in =	+855	Total energy out =	−1172

ΔH = +855−1172 = **−317 kJ mol⁻¹**

(g)

Bonds broken		New bonds formed	
4 mol C−H = 4 x 412	= 1648	2 mol C=O = 2 x 743	= 1486
2 mol O=O = 2 x 498	= 996	4 mol O−H = 4 x 463	= 1852
Total energy in =	+2644	Total energy out =	−3338

ΔH = +2644−3338 = **−694 kJ mol⁻¹**

(h)

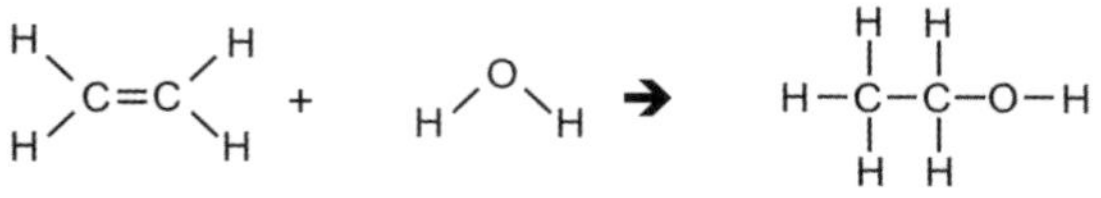

Bonds broken		New bonds formed	
1 mol C=C	= 612	1 mol C−C	= 348
1 mol O−H	= 463	1 mol C−H	= 412
		1 mol C−O	= 360
Total energy in =	+1075	Total energy out =	−1120

ΔH = +1075−1120 = **−45 kJ mol⁻¹**

(i)

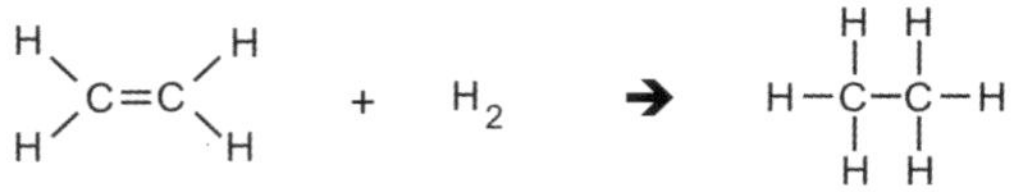

$H_2C=CH_2$ + H_2 → CH_3-CH_3

Bonds broken

1 mol C=C	= 612
1 mol H–H	= 436
Total energy in =	+1048

New bonds formed

1 mol C–C	= 348
2 mol C–H = 2 x 412	= 824
Total energy out =	−1172

ΔH = +1048−1172 = **−124 kJ mol^{-1}**

(j)

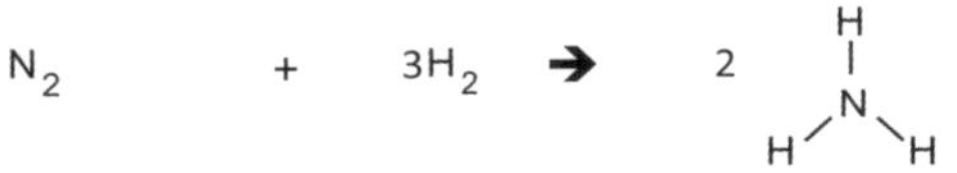

N_2 + $3H_2$ → 2 NH_3

Bonds broken

1 mol N≡N	= 945
3 mol H–H = 3 x 436	= 1308
Total energy in =	+2253

New bonds formed

6 mol N–H = 6 x 388	= 2328
Total energy out =	−2328

ΔH = +2253−2328 = **−75 kJ mol^{-1}**

(k)

H_2 + Cl_2 → 2HCl

Bonds broken

1 mol H–H	= 436
1 mol Cl–Cl	= 243
Total energy in =	+679

New bonds formed

2 mol H–Cl = 2 x 432	= 864
Total energy out =	−864

ΔH = +679−864 = **−185 kJ mol^{-1}**

(l)

Bonds broken

1 mol C=C	= 612
1 mol H–Br	= 366
Total energy in =	+978

New bonds formed

1 mol C–C	= 348
1 mol C–Br	= 276
1 mol C–H	= 412
Total energy out =	−1036

ΔH = +978−1036 = **−58 kJ mol^{-1}**

Oxidation and reduction (revision)

1. (a) Oxidation is the **loss of electrons** by a reactant.
   (b) Reduction is the **gain of electrons** by a reactant.

2. (a) A metal element reacting to form a compound is an example of **oxidation**.
   (b) A compound reacting to form a metal element is an example of **reduction**.

3. (a) $Mg\,(s)\ \rightarrow\ Mg^{2+}\,(aq)\ +\ 2e^-$
   (b) $Fe^{2+}\,(aq)\ \rightarrow\ Fe^{3+}\,(aq)\ +\ e^-$
   (c) $2I^-\,(aq)\ \rightarrow\ I_2\,(s)\ +\ 2e^-$
   (d) $Al^{3+}\,(aq)\ +\ 3e^-\ \rightarrow\ Al\,(s)$
   (e) $Cl_2\,(g)\ +\ 2e^-\ \rightarrow\ 2Cl^-\,(aq)$
   (f) $Cr_2O_7^{2-}\,(aq)\ +\ 14H^+\,(aq)\ +\ 6e^-\ \rightarrow\ 2Cr^{3+}\,(aq)\ +\ 7H_2O\,(l)$

Redox reactions

1.   Redox reactions involve the transfer of electrons from one atom, molecule or ion to another.

> **Reminder:**
> To obtain an overall equation for a redox reaction it is necessary to combine the ion-electron equations for the oxidation and reduction steps.
> Before adding it may be necessary to multiply one or both equations by a factor to ensure the number of electrons in the oxidation step cancels out the number of electrons in the reduction step.

2.   (a) The first equation (the oxidation step) must be multiplied throughout by 2, and the second equation (the reduction step) by 3.
        Adding then gives the following redox equation:
        $2Al\,(s) + 6H^+\,(aq) \rightarrow 2Al^{3+}\,(aq) + 3H_2\,(g)$
        [Note: The redox equation does not show the cancelled electrons.]

        (b) (2 x Equation 1) + Equation 2 gives
        $2Ce^{4+}\,(aq) + 2Br^-\,(aq) \rightarrow 2Ce^{3+}\,(aq) + Br_2\,(g)$

        (c) Equation 1 + (2 x Equation 2) gives
        $Cu\,(s) + 2Ag^+\,(aq) \rightarrow Cu^{2+}\,(aq) + 2Ag\,(s)$

        (d) *Equation 1 in question should have $4H_2O\,(l)$ as a product.*

        Equation 1 + (5 x Equation 2) gives
        $MnO_4^-\,(aq) + 8H^+\,(aq) + 5Fe^{2+}\,(aq) \rightarrow Mn^{2+}\,(aq) + 4H_2O\,(l) + 5Fe^{3+}\,(aq)$

        (e) Equation 1 + (3 x Equation 2) gives
        $Cr_2O_7^{2-}\,(aq) + 14H^+\,(aq) + 3Sn^{2+}\,(aq) \rightarrow 2Cr^{3+}\,(aq) + 7H_2O\,(l) + 3Sn^{4+}\,(aq)$

3.   Oxidation step   Reduction step
        (a) $Fe^{2+}\,(aq) \rightarrow Fe^{3+}\,(aq) + e^-$ $Cl_2\,(g) + 2e^- \rightarrow 2Cl^-\,(aq)$
        [Although the oxidation step actually involves **two** Fe^{2+} ions losing **two** electrons to form **two** Fe^{3+} ions, it is normal to write the ion-electron equation in the "cancelled down" form.]

        (b) $Zn\,(s) \rightarrow Zn^{2+}\,(aq) + 2e^-$ $Cu^{2+}\,(aq) + 2e^- \rightarrow Cu\,(s)$

        (c) $Mg\,(s) \rightarrow Mg^{2+}\,(aq) + 2e^-$ $2H^+\,(aq) + 2e^- \rightarrow H_2\,(g)$

3. Oxidation step   Reduction step
    [Spectator ions, e.g. K^+ ions in (d), NO_3^- in (e), Cl^- in (f) and Na^+ in (g) do **not** appear in the ion-electron equations.]

(d) $2Br^- (aq) \rightarrow Br_2 (aq) + 2e^-$ $Cl_2 (g) + 2e^- \rightarrow 2Cl^- (aq)$

(e) $Cu (s) \rightarrow Cu^{2+} (aq) + 2e^-$ $2Ag^+ (aq) + 2e^- \rightarrow 2Ag (s)$

(f) $Fe (s) \rightarrow Fe^{2+} (aq) + 2e^-$ $2H^+ (aq) + 2e^- \rightarrow H_2 (g)$

(g) Oxidation step: $SO_3^{2-} (aq) + H_2O (l) \rightarrow SO_4^{2-} (aq) + 2H^+ (aq) + 2e^-$
    Reduction step: $I_2 (aq) + 2e^- \rightarrow 2I^- (aq)$

(h) Oxidation step: $Fe^{2+} (aq) \rightarrow Fe^{3+} (aq) + e^-$
    Reduction step: $Cr_2O_7^{2-} (aq) + 14H^+ (aq) + 6e^- \rightarrow 2Cr^{3+} (aq) + 7H_2O (l)$

4. (a) $Pd^{2+} + 2e^- \rightarrow Pd$
    (b) $2CO (g) + O_2 (g) \rightarrow 2CO_2 (g)$

5. (a) Oxidation step: $Zn (s) \rightarrow Zn^{2+} (aq) + 2e^-$
    Reduction step: $Ag^+ (aq) + e^- \rightarrow Ag (s)$
    Redox equation: $Zn (s) + 2Ag^+ (aq) \rightarrow Zn^{2+} (aq) + 2Ag (s)$

(b) Oxidation step: $2I^- (aq) \rightarrow I_2 (s) + 2e^-$
    Reduction step: $Cl_2 (g) + 2e^- \rightarrow 2Cl^- (aq)$
    Redox equation: $2I^- (aq) + Cl_2 (g) \rightarrow I_2 (s) + 2Cl^V (aq)$

(c) Oxidation step: $Mg (s) \rightarrow Mg^{2+} (aq) + 2e^-$
    Reduction step: $2H^+ (aq) + 2e^- \rightarrow H_2 (g)$
    Redox equation: $Mg (s) + 2H^+ (aq) \rightarrow Mg^{2+} (aq) + H_2 (g)$

(d) Oxidation step: $SO_3^{2-} (aq) + H_2O (l) \rightarrow SO_4^{2-} (aq) + 2H^+ (aq) + 2e^-$
    Reduction step: $Br_2 (aq) + 2e^- \rightarrow 2Br^- (aq)$
    Redox equation:
    $SO_3^{2-} (aq) + H_2O (l) + Br_2 (aq) \rightarrow SO_4^{2-} (aq) + 2H^+ (aq) + 2Br^- (aq)$

(e) Oxidation step: $Fe^{2+} (aq) \rightarrow Fe^{3+} (aq) + e^-$
    Reduction step: $MnO_4^- (aq) + 8H^+ (aq) + 5e^- \rightarrow Mn^{2+} (aq) + 4H_2O (l)$
    Redox equation:
    $MnO_4^- (aq) + 8H^+ (aq) + 5Fe^{2+} (aq) \rightarrow Mn^{2+} (aq) + 3H_2O (l) + 5Fe^{3+} (aq)$

5. (f) Oxidation step: Sn^{2+} (aq) → Sn^{4+} (aq) + 2e⁻
        Reduction step: $Cr_2O_7^{2-}$ (aq) + 14H⁺ (aq) + 6e⁻ → $2Cr^{3+}$ (aq) + $7H_2O$ (l)
        Redox equation:
        $3Sn^{2+}$ (aq) + $Cr_2O_7^{2-}$ (aq) + 14H⁺ (aq) → $3Sn^{4+}$ (aq) + $2Cr^{3+}$ (aq) + $7H_2O$ (l)

    (g) Oxidation step: SO_3^{2-} (aq) + H_2O (l) → SO_4^{2-} (aq) + 2H⁺ (aq) + 2e⁻
        Reduction step: Br_2 (aq) + 2e⁻ → 2Br⁻ (aq)
        Redox equation:
        SO_3^{2-} (aq) + H_2O (l) + Br_2 (aq) → SO_4^{2-} (aq) + 2H⁺ (aq) + 2Br⁻ (aq)
        [Na⁺ (aq) is a spectator ion.]

    (h) Oxidation step: 2I⁻ (aq) → I_2 (s) + 2e⁻
        Reduction step: Cl_2 (g) + 2e⁻ → 2Cl⁻ (aq)
        Redox equation: 2I⁻ (aq) + Cl_2 (g) → I_2 (s) + 2Cl⁻ (aq)
        [K⁺ (aq) is a spectator ion.]

    (i) Oxidation step: 2Cl- (aq) → Cl_2 (g) + 2e⁻
        Reduction step: MnO_4^- (aq) + 8H⁺ (aq) + 5e⁻ → Mn^{2+} (aq) + $4H_2O$ (l)
        Redox equation:
        $2MnO_4^-$ (aq) + 16H⁺ (aq) + 10Cl⁻ (aq) → $2Mn^{2+}$ (aq) + $8H_2O$ (l) + $5Cl_2$ (g)
        [K⁺ (aq) is a spectator ion.]

    (j) Oxidation step: SO_3^{2-} (aq) + H_2O (l) → SO_4^{2-} (aq) + 2H⁺ (aq) + 2e⁻
        Reduction step: $Cr_2O_7^{2-}$ (aq) + 14H⁺ (aq) + 6e⁻ → $2Cr^{3+}$ (aq) + $7H_2O$ (l)
        Redox equation:
        $3SO_3^{2-}$ (aq) + $Cr_2O_7^{2-}$ (aq) + 8H⁺ (aq) → $3SO_4^{2-}$ (aq) + $2Cr^{3+}$ (aq) + $4H_2O$ (l)
        [K⁺ (aq) and Na⁺ (aq) are spectator ions.]

    (k) Oxidation step: 2Br⁻ (aq) → Br_2 (aq) + 2e⁻
        Reduction step: MnO_4^- (aq) + 8H⁺ (aq) + 5e⁻ → Mn^{2+} (aq) + $4H_2O$ (l)
        Redox equation:
        $2MnO_4^-$ (aq) + 16H⁺ (aq) + 10Br⁻ (aq) → $2Mn^{2+}$ (aq) + $8H_2O$ (l) + $5Br_2$ (g)
        [K⁺ (aq) and Na⁺ (aq) are spectator ions.]

Writing ion-electron equations

Reminder: The following steps are necessary to write and balance ion-electron
equations from the reactant and product.
Step 1 – Balance the element that is not hydrogen or oxygen.
Step 2 – Balance oxygen by adding H_2O molecules to the appropriate side.
Step 3 – Balance hydrogen by adding H^+ ions to the appropriate side.
Step 4 – Balance the electrical charge on each side by adding electrons.
[The overall electrical charge must be the same on both sides, but not necessarily
zero.]

1. (a) Step 1 – SO_3^{2-} (aq) → SO_4^{2-} (aq)
    [1 sulphur on both sides no need to balance.]
    Step 2 – SO_3^{2-} (aq) + H_2O (l) → SO_4^{2-} (aq)
    [1 water molecule added to left side to balance oxygen.]
    Step 3 – SO_3^{2-} (aq) + H_2O (l) → SO_4^{2-} (aq) + $2H^+$ (aq)
    [2 hydrogen ions added to right side to balance hydrogen.]
    Step 4 – SO_3^{2-} (aq) + H_2O (l) → SO_4^{2-} (aq) + $2H^+$ (aq) + $2e^-$
    [2 electrons added to right side to balance electrical charge (2– on both
    sides)]

    Following the same procedure gives the following balanced ion-electron
    equations for (b) to (g).

    (b) MnO_4^- (aq) + $8H^+$ (aq) + $5e^-$ → Mn^{2+} (aq) + $4H_2O$ (l)
    (c) $2IO_3^-$ (aq) + $12H^+$ (aq) + $10e^-$ → I_2 (aq) + $6H_2O$ (l)
    (d) PbO_2 (s) + $4H^+$ (aq) + $2e^-$ → Pb^{2+} (aq) + $2H_2O$ (l)
    (e) XeO_3 (aq) + $6H^+$ (aq) + $6e^-$ → Xe (g) + $3H_2O$ (l)
    (f) ClO^- (aq) + $2H^+$ (aq) + $2e^-$ → Cl^- (aq) + H_2O (l)
    (g) $Cr_2O_7^{2-}$ (aq) + $14H^+$ (aq) + $6e^-$ → $2Cr^{3+}$ (aq) + $7H_2O$ (l)

2. $2CH_2CHCN$ + $2H_2O$ (l) + $2e^-$ → $(CH_2CH_2CN)_2$ + $2OH^-$ (aq)

Oxidising and reducing agents

1. (a) An oxidising agent is a substance that accepts electrons. It brings about oxidation and is reduced in a redox reaction.
    (b) A reducing agent is a substance that donates electrons. It brings about reduction and is oxidised in a redox reaction.

2. (a) **Examples**: hydrogen peroxide (H_2O_2), sodium hypochlorite (NaOCl), potassium permanganate ($KMnO_4$), sulphur dioxide (SO_2)

    (b) Hydrogen peroxide is a strong oxidising agent. It is used in everyday life to break down coloured compounds and remove their colour, e.g. from clothes or hair.
    Sodium hypochlorite is a strong oxidising agent used in everyday life as a bleaching agent and disinfectant.
    More generally oxidising agents are widely employed because of their effectiveness in killing bacteria and inactivating viruses.
    Potassium permanganate is an oxidising agent that will react with any organic matter in a pond, including algae, sediments and bacteria. It can also be used to treat common diseases of fish such as bacterial or fungal infections.
    Sulphur dioxide is an oxidising agent that can be used in bleaching reactions.

3.

	Oxidising agent (Electron acceptor)	Reducing agent (Electron donor)
(a)	Cl_2 (g)	Br^- (aq)
(b)	Cu^{2+} (aq)	Mg (s)
(c)	H^+ (aq)	Fe (s)
(d)	Br_2 (g)	I^- (aq)
(e)	H^+ (aq)	Zn (s)
(f)	I_2 (aq)	SO_3^{2-} (aq)
(g)	$Cr_2O_7^{2-}$ (aq) / H^+ (aq) i.e. acidified dichromate solution [The presence of the H^+ ions is essential.]	Fe^{2+} (aq)

Neutralisation (revision)

Reminder 1: $n = C \times V$ or no. of moles = conc. $\times$ litres
Reminder 2: $V = \dfrac{n}{C}$ or litres = $\dfrac{\text{no. of moles}}{\text{conc.}}$
Reminder 3: $C = \dfrac{n}{V}$ or conc. = $\dfrac{\text{no. of moles}}{\text{litres}}$

1.   (a) $n = C \times V = 0.1 \times 0.025 = $ **0.0025 mol**

     (b)   1 mol of NaOH neutralises 1 mol of HCl [from balanced equation]
Therefore, no. of moles of HCl = 0.0025 [from (a)]
$C = \dfrac{n}{V} = 0.0025 \div 0.0374 = $ **0.067 mol l^{-1}**

2.   (a)   1 mol of NaOH neutralises 1 mol of HCl [from balanced equation]
No. of moles of NaOH $= 0.2 \times 0.05 = 0.01$
Therefore, no. of moles of HCl = 0.01
$V = \dfrac{n}{C} = 0.01 \div 0.01 = $ **1 litre**

     (b)   1 mol of H_2SO_4 neutralises 2 mol of KOH [from balanced equation]
No. of moles of KOH $= 1 \times 0.025 = 0.025$
Therefore, no. of moles of $H_2SO_4 = 0.0125$
$C = \dfrac{n}{V} = 0.0125 \div 0.05 = $ **0.25 mol l^{-1}**

3.   (a) $HCl\,(aq) + KOH\,(aq) \rightarrow KCl\,(aq) + H_2O\,(l)$
1 mol of HCl neutralises 1 mol KOH
No. of moles of KOH $= 0.1 \times 0.02 = 0.002$
Therefore, no. of moles of HCl = 0.002
$C = \dfrac{n}{V} = 0.002 \div 0.0126 = $ **0.159 mol l^{-1}**

     (b) $HNO_3\,(aq) + NaOH\,(aq) \rightarrow NaNO_3\,(aq) + H_2O\,(l)$
1 mol of HNO_3 neutralises 1 mol NaOH
No. of moles of NaOH $= 0.5 \times 0.02 = 0.01$
Therefore, no. of moles of $HNO_3 = 0.01$
$V = \dfrac{n}{C} = 0.01 \div 2 = $ **0.005 litres (or 5 cm^3)**

3. (c) H_2SO_4 (aq) + 2NaOH (aq) → Na_2SO_4 (aq) + $2H_2O$ (l)
    1 mol of H_2SO_4 neutralises 2 mol of NaOH
    No. of moles of NaOH = C x V = 0.5 x 0.025 = 0.0125
    Therefore, no. of moles of HSO_4 = 0.0125 ÷ 2 = 0.00625
    C = $\underline{n}$ = 0.00625 ÷ 0.0173 = **0.361 mol l^{-1}**
    $\quad$ V

4. (a) n = 0.1 x 0.020 = **0.002 mol**

    (b) 1 mol of ethanoic acid reacts with 1 mol of sodium hydroxide.
    Therefore, from (a), number of moles of ethanoic acid = 0.002
    C = $\underline{n}$ = 0.002 ÷ 0.025 = **0.08 mol l^{-1}**
    $\quad$ V

5. $\quad$ 1 mol of H_2SO_4 neutralises 2 mol of NH_3 [from balanced equation]
    No. of moles of NH_3 = C x V = 0.5 x 0.020 = 0.01
    Therefore, no. of moles of H_2SO_4 = 0.005
    V = $\underline{n}$ = 0.005 ÷ 0.5 = **0.01 litres (or 10 cm^3)**
    $\quad$ C

6. $\quad$ 1 mol of calcium ions reacts with 1 mol of EDTA
    No. of moles of EDTA = C x V = 0.12 x 0.0186 = 0.002232 (or 2.232 x 10^{-3})
    Therefore, no. of moles of calcium ions = 0.002232
    C = $\underline{n}$ = 0.002232 ÷ 0.025 = **0.0893 mol l^{-1}**
    $\quad$ V

Redox titrations

1.   [from balanced equation]
        6 mol of Fe^{2+} ions react with 1 mol of $Cr_2O_7^{2-}$ (dichromate) ions
        No. of moles of $Cr_2O_7^{2-}$ ions $= C \times V = 0.1 \times 0.25 = 0.025$
        Therefore, no. of moles of Fe^{2+} ions $= 6 \times 0.025 = \textbf{0.15 mol}$

2.   [from balanced equation]
        2 mol of MnO_4^- (permanganate) ions react with 5 mol of H_2O_2
        No. of moles of MnO_4^- ions $= C \times V = 0.1 \times 0.016 = 0.0016$
        Therefore, no. of moles of $H_2O_2 = (5 \div 2) \times 0.0016 = 0.004$
        $C = \dfrac{n}{V} = 0.004 \div 0.025 = \textbf{0.16 mol l}^{-1}$

3.   [from balanced equation]
        3 mol of ethanol (C_2H_5OH) react with 2 mol of $Cr_2O_7^{2-}$ ions
        No. of moles of $Cr_2O_7^{2-}$ ions $= C \times V = 0.1 \times 0.0125 = 0.00125$
        Therefore, no. of moles of ethanol $= (3 \div 2) \times 0.00125 = 0.001875$
        But, 1 mol of ethanol (C_2H_5OH) $= (2 \times 12) + (6 \times 1) + 16 = 46$ g
        Therefore, mass of ethanol in 1 cm^3 of wine sample
        $M = n \times GFM = 0.001875 \times 46 = \textbf{0.086 g}$

4.   [from balanced equation]
        1 mol of Cl_2 reacts with 2 mol of Fe^{2+} ions
        No. of moles of $Fe^{2+} = C \times V = 2.82 \times 0.0249 = 0.070218$
        Therefore, no. of moles of Cl_2 in 100 cm^3 of water $= 0.035109$
        But, 1 mole of $Cl_2 = (2 \times 35.5) = 71$ g
        Therefore, mass of Cl_2 in 100 cm^3 of water
        $M = n \times GFM = = 0.035109 \times 71 = 2.49$ g
        Therefore, concentration of $Cl_2 = \textbf{24.9 g l}^{-1}$

5.   [from balanced equation]

1 mol of Fe^{2+} ions react with 1 mol of Ce^{4+} ions

No. of moles of Fe^{2+} = C x V = 0.05 x 0.00485 = 2.425×10^{-4}

Therefore, no. of moles of Ce^{4+} in 10 cm^3 sample of solution = 2.425×10^{-4}

Therefore, no. of moles of Ce^{4+} in the full 30 cm^3 of solution = $3 \times 2.425 \times 10^{-4}$

But, 1 mole of Ce^{4+} = 140.1 g

Therefore, mass of cerium in the flint

M = n x GFM = $3 \times 2.425 \times 10^{-4} \times 140.1$ g = **0.102 g**

6.   [from balanced equation]

1 mol of SO_2 reacts with 1 mol of I_2

No. of moles of I_2 = C x V = 0.005 x 0.0112 = 5.6×10^{-5}

Therefore, no. of moles of SO_2 = 5.6×10^{-5} (in 100 cm^3 of wine)

But, 1 mol of SO_2 = 32.1 + (2 x 16) = 64.1 g

Therefore, mass of SO_2 in 100 cm^3 of wine

M = n x GFM = $5.6 \times 10^{-5} \times 64.1$ g

Therefore, mass of SO_2 in 1 litre of wine = $10 \times 5.6 \times 10^{-5} \times 64.1$

                             = 0.0359 g

            or SO_2 concentration of **35.9 mg l^{-1}**

7.   [from balanced equation]

1 mol of O_3 → 1 mol of I_2 which reacts with 2 mol of $S_2O_3^{2-}$ (thiosulphate)

No. of moles of $S_2O_3^{2-}$ = C x V = 0.01 x 0.0225 = 2.25×10^{-4}

Therefore, no. of moles of O_3 in 10^5 litres of air = 1.125×10^{-4}

Therefore, volume of O_3 in 10^5 litres of air = $1.125 \times 10^{-4} \times 24$ litres

Therefore, volume of O_3 in 1 litre of air

                         = $(1.125 \times 10^{-4} \times 24) \div 10^5$ = **2.7×10^{-8} litres**

8.   [from balanced equation]

1 mol of vitamin C ($C_6H_8O_6$) reacts with 1 mol of I_2

No. of moles of I_2 = C x V = 0.02 x 0.0295 = 5.9×10^{-4}

Therefore, no. of moles of vitamin C = 5.9×10^{-4}

But, 1 mole of vitamin C ($C_6H_8O_6$) = (6 x 12) + (8 x 1) + (6 x 16) = 176 g

Therefore, mass of vitamin C in 25 cm^3 of solution

M = n x GFM = $5.9 \times 10^{-4} \times 176$ g = **0.104 g**

9.   [from balanced equation]
5 mol of Fe^{2+} react with 1 mol of MnO_4^-
No. of moles of MnO_4^- = C x V = 0.01 x 0.0095 = 9.5×10^{-5}
Therefore, no. of moles of Fe^{2+} = 5 x 9.5×10^{-5} = 4.75×10^{-4} (in 25 cm^3)
Therefore, 250 cm^3 of $FeSO_4.7H_2O$ contained 4.75×10^{-3} mol
But, 1 mol of $FeSO_4.7H_2O$ = 55.8 + 32.1 + (4 x 16) + 7 x [(2 x 1) + 16)]
                                                                    = 277.9 g

Therefore, mass of $FeSO_4.7H_2O$ (pure salt)
M = N x GFM = 4.75×10^{-3} x 277.9 = 1.32 g
Therefore, percentage purity = $\dfrac{\text{mass of pure salt}}{\text{mass of impure salt}}$ x 100

= (1.32 ÷ 1.55) x 100 = **85.2%**

Chromatography

1. (a) i) **X** is hexane (C_6H_{14}), **Y** is dodecane ($C_{12}H_{26}$) and **Z** is isocane ($C_{20}H_{42}$).
    ii) Molecules with a higher mass (assuming similar polarity) have a greater retention time and pass through more slowly.

    (b)
    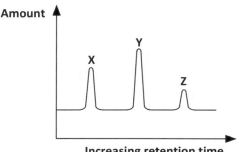

2. (a) i)
    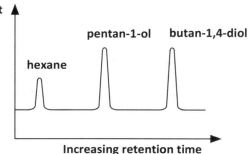

    ii) Hexane has only half the peak height of the other compounds because it has only half the volume.
    Hexane is non-polar and so has a shorter retention time than polar pentan-1-ol. Butane-1,4-diol is the most polar compound of the three and therefore has the greatest retention time.

    (b) The three compounds used have very similar molecular masses.
    Hexane – 86, pentan-1-ol – 88 and butane-1,4-diol – 90.
    Using an alcohol and a diol with six carbon atoms would unfairly involve compounds with considerably greater molecular mass, in an experiment to compare the effect of polarity on retention times.

3. (a) Compound **C**.
   (b) i) Structures **A** and **B** are similar.
      ii) The peaks for **A** and **B** are very close and partly overlap. As the the area under the peak gives a measure of the amount of each substance, accurate determination of the relative amounts is difficult.

4. (a) Glycine is likely to have the most polar structure.
      [It has travelled the least distance up the paper.]
   (b) **X** is phenylalanine; **Y** is asparagine; **Z** is glycine.
      In addition, all three are pure samples of the amino acid as all have only one spot.

Practical skills (i)

1. (a) A pipette accurately measures an exact volume of a liquid.
   A burette is used to accurately measure out variable volumes of liquid.
   (b) Draw liquid into the pipette, using a pipette filler, to above the mark on the pipette. Then release liquid until the bottom level of the meniscus just touches the mark on the pipette.

2. (a) A solution of accurately known concentration is known as a **standard solution**.
   (b) (1) Using a beaker accurately measure out the mass of substance required.
   (2) Add distilled water to completely dissolve the substance, stirring as required.
   (3) Pour the solution into a volumetric flask, and use a wash-bottle to rinse out any remaining drops from the beaker and stirring rod.
   (4) Add distilled water to just below the line on the volumetric flask.
   (5) Using a dropping pipette add more water until the bottom of the meniscus is on the mark on the flask.
   (c) Distilled (or deionised) water does not add any impurities to the standard solution.
   (d) Solids for making standard solutions would be unsuitable if they were not pure or completely dry.

3. (a) Very low concentration standard solutions are not made from solids due to the likely greater percentage error in making very small measurements.
   (b) A 1 mg l^{-1} solution is more accurately prepared by dilution of a more concentration solution, e.g. a 10 g l^{-1} solution.

4. (a) The end-point is the point at which the reaction is just complete when all the reactant has been used up.
   (b) An indicator detects the end-point of a titration by immediately changing colour at the point when excess reactant from the burette has been added.
   (c) In a self-indicating titration, the reactants produce an obvious colour change at the end-point without the need of an indicator.

5. (a) A rough titration is carried out first to give an approximate idea of the volume of liquid that must be added to reach the end-point.
Accurate titrations are then carried out.

(b) The student would know when to stop adding acid from the burette by using an indicator.

(c) 26.9 cm^3
[This is the average of the two accurate titrations (2 and 3) that agree to within 0.2 cm^3 of each other. The result of the rough titration (27.7) is NEVER used in the calculation.]

6. (a) The vitamin C solution would be transferred to the standard flask.
A wash bottle would then be used to rinse out any remaining drops of the vitamin C solution from the beaker and stirring rod.

(b) Any of the following are bad practice in technique:
(1) Failure to wear eye protection.
(2) Failure to remove the funnel from the burette.
(3) No sign of a pipette filler having been used.
(4) Burette reading being taken from the wrong angle.
(5) Protective laboratory coat is not buttoned and is not giving protection.
(6) Pipette is placed where it could roll from the bench.
(7) Clamped burette on the stand looks unstable and likely to fall over.

Practical skills (ii)

1.
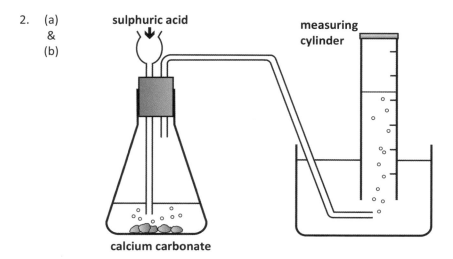

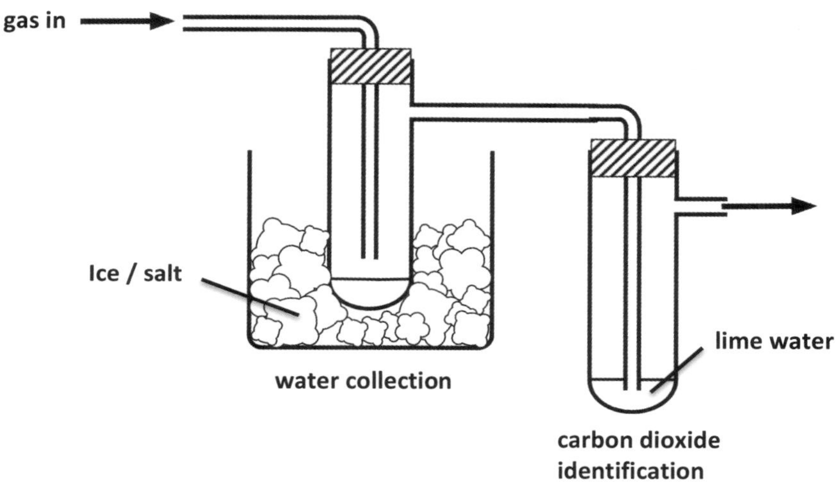

gas in

Ice / salt

water collection

lime water

carbon dioxide
identification

2. (a)
   &
   (b)

sulphuric acid

measuring
cylinder

calcium carbonate

(c) All of the following variables would need to be controlled.
   (1) Mass of calcium carbonate used.
   (2) Concentration of sulphuric acid.
   (3) Volume of sulphuric acid.
   (4) Temperature of the sulphuric acid.

3.

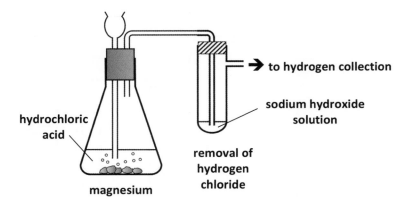

hydrochloric acid

magnesium

removal of hydrogen chloride

to hydrogen collection

sodium hydroxide solution

4. (a)

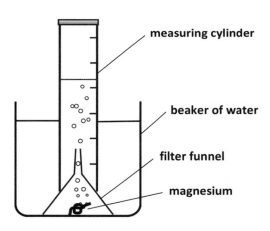

measuring cylinder

beaker of water

filter funnel

magnesium

(b) The measurements that would have to be taken are:
(1) the starting mass of magnesium ribbon and the mass of any remaining magnesium ribbon. [These measurements would allow the mass of magnesium used to be calculated.]
(2) the volume of hydrogen gas collected

5.

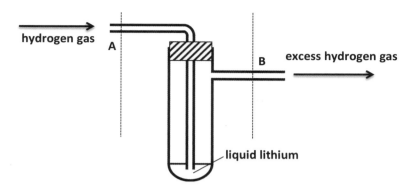

hydrogen gas   A

B   excess hydrogen gas

liquid lithium

6.   Using one of the liquids, measure the paddle speed by counting the turns per minute for a certain reading on the speed controller.
Change the liquid in the measuring cylinder (keeping the volume the same).
Keeping the reading on the speed controller the same, measure the new paddle speed.
A more viscous liquid will slow down the paddle and give fewer turns per minute.

OR

Using one of the liquids, measure the paddle speed by counting the turns per minute for a certain reading on the speed controller.
Change the liquid in the measuring cylinder (keeping the volume the same).
Adjust the speed controller to keep the paddle speed the same.
A more viscous liquid will require a higher reading on the speed controller to give the same paddle speed.

Problem solving: miscellaneous

1. (a) **A** is sodium hydroxide solution; **B** is sodium hydroxide solution;
        C is aluminium oxide.
    (b) **X** is digestion (under pressure); **Y** is filtration;
        Z is roasting (in rotary kiln).

2.   **A** – ammonia; **B** – water; **C** – nitric oxide; **D** – oxygen;
        E – nitrogen dioxide; **F** – sulphurous acid; **G** – sulphur;
        H – sulphur dioxide; **I** – water.

3.

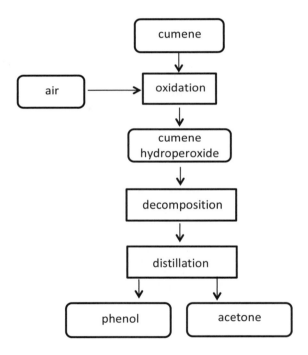

4. (a) tetra-atomic
    (b) ethene (C_2H_4)
    (c) CH_2Cl_2

5. (a) The number of X=O bonds appears to determine the strength of the acid. The greater the number of these bonds the stronger the acid.

(b)

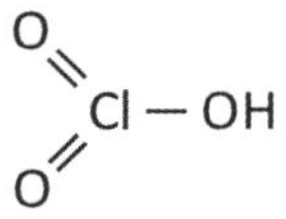

6.   A = Sodium sulphate(VI)   B = KIO_4 C = +5
        D = Sodium phosphate(V)   E = 3−

7. (a) P = 6   Q = Cu^{2+} R = 4−   S = $H_2N–CH_2–CH_2–NH_2$ $(C_2N_2H_8)$
    (b) i) The student would prepare eleven 10 cm^3 mixtures of nickel(II) sulphate solution and ammonia solution.
         The first 10 cm^3 mixture would contain 10 cm^3 of nickel(II) sulphate solution and 0 cm^3 of ammonia solution; the second 9 and 1; the third 8 and 2 and so on.
         A colorimeter would then be used to measure the intensity of the light transmitted through each mixture.

         ii) The highest colour intensity occurs when the ratio of ammonia to nickel(II) sulphate is 8.4 : 1.6 (from graph) or just over 5 to 1.

8. (a)

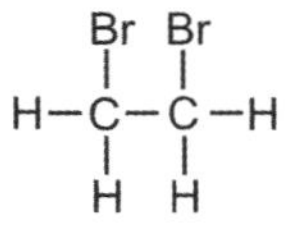

    (b)

    (c)

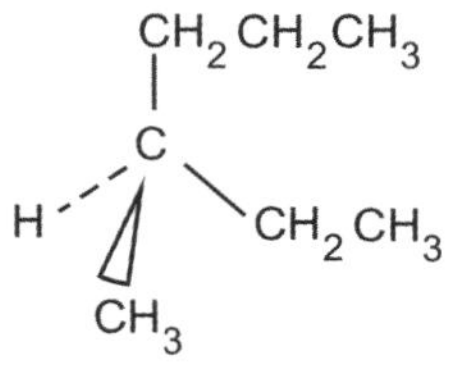

9. (a) **F** (Peak at 45) =

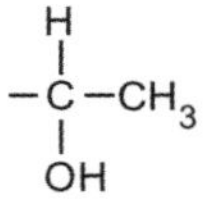

$$-\underset{\underset{\text{OH}}{|}}{\overset{\overset{\text{H}}{|}}{\text{C}}}-\text{CH}_3$$

G (Peak at 59) = $\text{CH}_3-\text{CH}_2-\underset{\underset{\text{OH}}{|}}{\overset{\overset{\text{H}}{|}}{\text{C}}}-$

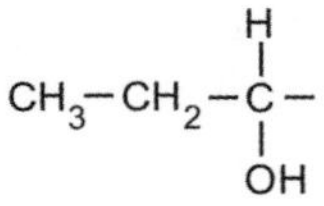

(b) The peaks at 44, 43, 42 and 41 are caused by the same fragment causing the peak at 45, i.e. $\text{CH(OH)}-\text{CH}_3$ with 1 to 4 additional hydrogen atoms removed.

10. (a) The hydrogen atoms do not show up clearly as they have no electrons other than the shared electrons joining them to the remainder of the molecule, and so the electron density is very low.

(b)

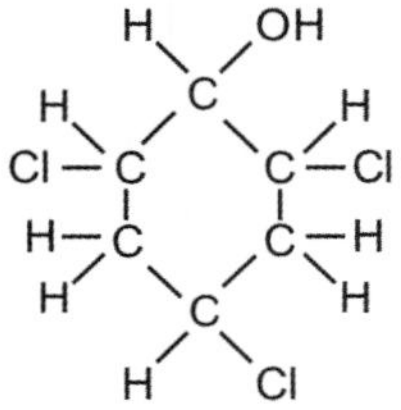

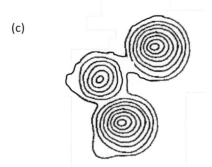

(c)

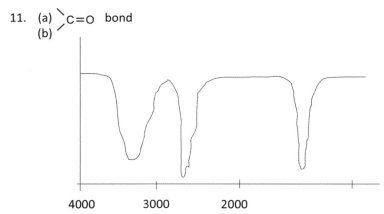

11. (a) $\overset{\diagdown}{\underset{\diagup}{\text{C}}}=\text{O}$ bond

(b)

Chemistry in Society

12. (a) The temperature of the test thermocouple is higher than the temperature of the reference thermocouple. Therefore the decomposition has released energy and the reaction is exothermic.
    (b) It must be stable to heat over a large temperature range.
    (c)

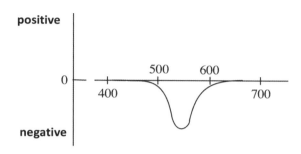

13. (a) **Acid** H_2O **Base** H_2O
    (b) an acid

    The formula for the bicarbonate ion should be HCO_3^- not HCO^{3-}.

14. (a)

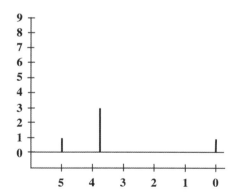

    (b)

15. (a) Radius ratio of magnesium oxide =
    Radius of Mg^{2+} ion ÷ Radius of O^{2-} ion = 72 ÷ 140 = **0.514**
    Therefore, magnesium oxide is more likely to have the same arrangement as **sodium chloride**, as the radius ratios are almost the same.
    (b) The smaller the ions the greater the enthalpy of lattice breaking.

Chemical arithmetic

1. (a) Average mass of iron = (3.2 + 3.0 + 2.6 + 3.4) ÷ 4 = 12.2 ÷ 4 = **3.05 mg**
    (b) Percentage of the RDA in Sample 1 = (3.2 ÷ 8) x 100 = **40%**

2. 30% of the RDA for vitamin C = (30 ÷ 100) x 80 mg = 24 mg.
    A 100 g portion of cereal contains 48 mg of vitamin C.
    Therefore, a **50 g** portion of cereal gives 24 mg (30% of RDA) of vitamin C.

3. Mass of liquid air to give 300 000 kg of nitrogen =
    (100 ÷ 78.7) x 300 000 = **381 194 kg**
    [Note: 78.7% of 381 194 = 300 000]

4. 100 cm^3 of milk contains 124 mg of calcium.
    Therefore, 250 cm^3 of milk contains (250 ÷ 100) x 124 mg of calcium
    = 310 mg. This is equal to **31%** of the RDA of 1000 mg.

5. Maximum dose of active ingredient in 24 hours is 500 mg.
    Therefore, maximum dose in 12 hours is 250 mg.
    Since 200 cm^3 of the liquid mixture contains 7.4 g (7400 mg) of active
    ingredient, the maximum volume of liquid that could be taken in 12 hours
    = (250 ÷ 7400) x 200 cm^3 = **6.76 cm^3**

6. The alcohol limit for driving in Scotland is 50 mg per 100 cm^3 of blood.
    Therefore, 40% of alcohol limit = (40 ÷ 100) x 50 = 20 mg per 100 cm^3.
    To reduce blood alcohol level from 56 mg to this level of 20 mg would take
    (56 − 20) ÷ 16 hours = **2.25 hours**, as alcohol is removed from the body at
    16 mg per hour.
    [The man's blood alcohol level would reach 40% of the limit at 12.15 am.]

7. 1 g of methanol produces 21.3 kJ of energy.
    Therefore, 1 cm^3 (0.792 g) produces 0.792 x 21.3 = 16.87 kJ.
    Therefore, to produce 2.4 x 10^5 kJ of energy requires
    (2.4 x 10^5 ÷ 16.87) = 14 226 cm^3 of methanol.
    Since, 45 litres of methanol (45 000 cm^3) costs £90, the cost of producing
    2.4 x 10^5 kJ of energy = (14 226 ÷ 45 000) x £90 = **£28.45**

8. *The question should have asked for the volume of air, i.e. gas, not liquid air.*

    Volume = Mass ÷ Density
    Therefore, 100 kg (100 000 g) of oxygen has a volume
    = 100 000 g ÷ 0.0014 g cm^{-3} = 7.143 x 10^7 cm^3
    But, only 20.95% of air is oxygen, therefore the **volume of air** to give that volume of oxygen = 7.143 x 10^7 x (100 ÷ 20.95) cm^3
    = 3.41 x 10^8 cm^3 = **3.41 x 10^5 litres** (or 341 000 litres)

9. Mass = Volume x Density
    2 litres (2000 cm^3) of ethanol has a mass of 2000 x 0.79 = 1580 g
    1 g of ethanol burns to produce 24.6 kJ of energy
    Therefore, 1 bottle of ethanol produces 1580 x 24.6 = 38 868 kJ of energy at a cost of £9.36
    Therefore, the cost of producing 15 000 kJ of energy
    = (15 000 ÷ 38 868) x £9.36 = **£3.61**

10. Recommended daily allowance (RDA) of zinc is 10.0 mg.
    1.4 mg of zinc is provide by 25 g of cashew nuts.
    Therefore, 5.0 mg of zinc (50% of RDA) is provided by (5.0 ÷ 1.4) x 25
    = 89.3 g.
    As cashew nuts cost £1.37 for 175 g, the cost of providing 50% of RDA = (89.3 ÷ 175) x £1.37 = **£0.70** or 70 p

11. 36 lozenges have a mass of 134 g
    Therefore, 1 lozenge has a mass of (134 ÷ 36) = 3.722 g = 3722 mg
    Each lozenge contains 5.4 mg of active ingredient
    Therefore, percentage by mass of active ingredient
    = (5.4 ÷ 3722) x 100 = **1.45%**

12. Quality of 4 karat gold piece = (4 ÷ 24)
    Gold price in pounds per gram = (840 ÷ 31.1)
    Melt value in pounds = mass in grams x quality x gold price per gram
    = 450 x (4 ÷ 24) x (840 ÷ 31.1) = **£2026**

13. (a) Average mass = (2.0 + 1.6 + 5.4 + 9.0) ÷ 4 = **4.5 mg**
    (b) Mass of hyoscine in fatal dose = (2.0 + 1.6 + 5.4 + 9.0) ÷ (58 ÷ 100)
        = (18 ÷ 0.58) = **31.0 mg**
    (c) 5 grains of hyoscine = (5 x 64) = 320 mg and would cost £13.50
        Extracted hyoscine (18 mg) would cost
        (18 ÷ 320) x £13.50 = **£0.76** or 76p

Open questions

By their very nature, there are a wide variety of possible answers to open-ended questions and the given mark is related to the variety and accuracy of the relevant chemistry in the response. There may be strengths and weaknesses in the answers and, as far as possible, the focus when marking should be on the strengths, taking account of weaknesses (errors or omissions) only where they detract from the overall answer in a significant way. The guidance below should be taken into account to determine the quality of the answer.

3 marks: The answer demonstrates a good understanding of a wide variety of aspects relating to the chemistry involved. In this type of answer, the chemistry covered is correct or largely correct (any weaknesses are minor and do not detract from the overall response). It does not mean the answer has to be what might be termed an "excellent" or "complete" answer.

2 marks: The candidate has demonstrated a reasonable understanding of a variety of aspects relating to the chemistry involved. In this type of answer, the chemistry covered may be largely correct but has weaknesses that detract to a small extent from the overall response.

1 mark: The candidate has demonstrated a limited understanding of a few aspects relating to the chemistry involved. In this type of answer, only a little of the chemistry that is relevant to the problem/situation is understood and there may be weaknesses that significantly detract from the overall response.

0 marks: The candidate has demonstrated no understanding of the chemistry that is relevant to the problem/situation.